Russel Wright
DINNERWARE
Designs for the American Table

Ann Kerr

D1479091

COLLECTOR BOOKS
A Division of Schroeder Publishing Co., Inc.

The current values in this book should be used only as a guide. They are not intended to set prices, which vary from one section of the country to another. Auction prices as well as dealer prices vary greatly and are affected by condition as well as demand. Neither the Author nor the Publisher assumes responsibility for any losses that might be incurred as a result of consulting this guide.

Additional copies of this book may be ordered from:

Collector Books
P.O. Box 3009
Paducah, KY 42001

or

Ann Kerr
P.O. Box 437
Sidney, Ohio 45365

@$9.95 Add $1.00 for postage and handling.

Copyright: Ann Kerr, 1985
ISBN: 0-89145-292-3

This book or any part thereof may not be reproduced without the written consent of the Author and Publisher.

Dedicated to all those who sought out Russel Wright designs when they were made and who have held them precious across the years. May their faith be justified, their collections used again and their tribe increased with those who are discovering it for the first time.

In Appreciation

Everyone who attempts a project of this sort thanks their family, and I join them. While I've not turned our home into a pottery showroom, I have traveled a bit and my husband has resisted every impulse to ask "Is this trip necessary?". I am grateful for his restraint, sorry about his lonely meals and so appreciative of his surety that this project would succeed.

Our older daughter, Ann Peirce, a graphic designer, was a great help on this project with much cover input. I turned it over to her completely, trusting her judgement as I always do. She "came through" beautifully as she always does. Both she and her husband Greg have helped with the marks section.

Our son, David, shored me up emotionally with his "Go for it, Mom." His confidence means a great deal to me.

Susan, our younger daughter, has gone to shows and sales with me, showing promise of being a budding collector herself. Her companionship has brightened my days with shared pleasures.

My dear friend, Jo Cunningham, dreamed the dream with me early and remained with me late, supportive all along the way.

Karen and Hal Silvermintz gave me bed, board and good times shared over and over. Many of the things pictured are Karen's. Hal stepped out of his professional role as an Animator and worked out our really needed color charts. Additionally, he became our eastern photographer. He reminded me that he was an amateur in that field, but I find his pictures among the best here. Proof again that "home grown" is hard to beat. I'm never able to match the kindnesses I've received from the Silvermintzes.

Carolyn Davis and the staff at the George Ahrents Research Library at Syracuse University where the Wright papers are housed, went above and beyond in their help to me.

Christopher Wilk and staff at the Brooklyn Museum, and the Metropolitan Museum staff took interest in the project and helped where they were able. The New York Gallery Association dug deep to share photos and helped in every way I asked.

Annie Wright, Russel's daughter, led me to Russel's friends and associates - a great help. She gave me a wonderful picture of her father, which I cannot share because of copyright restrictions. Her support has meant a great deal.

Herbert Honig, Russel's friend and Business Manager, answered my day and night calls with the same "What can I do for you, my dear." His recollections are very significant to this work.

Irving Richards, who worked so closely with Wright and was the co-founder of Raymor, was generous with his comments and asked me to "call again."

Sharon and Bob Huxford, pottery editors of Collector Books, took early interest in this project. I am grateful to them as I am to all of the Collector Books people, most especially Steve Quertermous, who always reassured me I was approaching this all from the right angle.

Those who shared their collections for photographing are many: Ted Haun, Paul Walter, Bill Strauss, Pete Palm of Musicality in Cincinnati, and Stanley Coren of Beige in New York, Barbara Siemsen, John Moses, Naomi in San Francisco--all shared their dishes, thoughts, opinions and kindnesses. I'm grateful.

Especially helpful was B. A. Wellman, Massachusetts, who is the authority on Melmac dinnerware. He sent many examples and the wonderful Iroquois display sign is part of his extensive collection of pottery advertisement items.

Jack Williams of Mississippi, who owns the largest collection of Country Garden by Mary Wright, shared his entire collection with us, else we'd have few examples.

Jean Hutchison, Ed Fitzwater, Sandy Cohen, Ben Seibel and the late Arthur Harshman allowed me to jog their memories early and late. Their recollections were important to the text.

Couchman Photographers in Sidney, Ohio, were patient and ready to help on the spur of the moment. Helen Davis, my typist, read my mind when she couldn't read my writing, keeping ahead of me as I worked. My local help was invaluable.

Of course there are many more who sold me things and sent information all along the way over many years. My information came as "open stock", a dish here, an advertisement there, a magazine clipping now and again. It all helped to piece the story together, and I owe so much to so many.

The telling of all this combines the special contributions of so many dear friends. If it in any way fills a void in the collecting of Russel Wright designs, their trust in me will have been rewarded.

I thank each of you again.

Foreword

The place to begin a book, whether in writing it or reading it, I have decided, is at the beginning. In writing this I find that I am as impatient as you and am eager to skip these words, to get into pictures, descriptions and lists. However, I find I cannot accurately explain the genre of Russel Wright's dinnerware designs and the phenomena of its collectors without defining his philosophy, his aspirations, his business arrangements, his personal life and all the rest which combined to make him the most appreciated and most prolific American designer of the twentieth century.

I ask you then to bear with me now and promise that if we start out together in this writing, each page of pictures, each list of items will hold added meaning for us as we see in them the total application of his talent.

It is almost impossible to separate Russel Wright, the man, from the social philosophy which was almost a religion to him. He applied its principles to every object which he created and if he did not live it, it was not through lack of faith but that his self-conception differed from actuality. Every manufacturing achievement was a statement of this doctrine and cups and saucers become vessels of his ideology. He worked, aspired and achieved a total concept, and if we do not understand that, we miss much of the pleasure of collecting his designs.

It follows, then, that a collection of Russel Wright designs is a bit different from other collections we prize. Those who seek out his dinnerware soon find themselves looking for his glassware and it is a quick and easy step up to looking for his stainless steel and spun aluminum - and so on. In no time, the beginning collector finds he's collecting Russel Wright - the proper noun, and seeks out anything with that special signature. In that short transitional time, the same collector finds himself equally interested in the details about the designer himself and it's one short step further to understanding and appreciating the philosophy behind the designs.

I wish you total enjoyment in your Russel Wright collecting and can promise that if you'll not skip to the pictures and prices, the text as it follows will make each treasure you find a more meaningful addition to your collection. Let us begin.

Contents

Marks

Those who study marks, their dates and meanings, have a real challenge in the markings found on Russel Wright designs. I offer them here with what information is currently available or as marks found. In some instances I have only instant photographs (which will not reproduce well) and must add verbally to what is pictured. In the process of preparing this mark section, we learned that there are minute differences in the same mark, even to the signature detail. These are not important, but I call it to your attention for your study.

Both the Steubenville Pottery, which made American Modern, and Harker had only one mark. In most cases the number 1 Steubenville mark is deeply incised while the Harker mark shown here is so lightly cut that glaze appears to have run into the mark, all but filling it. We have drawn it here, but it will be found lightly incised number 2. Most American Modern and Harker are marked.

Russel Wright
MFG BY
STEUBENVILLE

HARKERWARE
by *Russel Wright*

Mark 1    **Mark 2**

The Iroquois marks pictured here are all inclusive, we believe, and we have good reason to believe we have them placed in their time sequence. The first two marks appear identical except for the treatment in the type used in the letter "I". The number 3 "loopy I" as we've come to call it, is the earlier of the two, and the number 4 straight "I", while an early mark, was later. Look for these in dark blue and brown on the heavier early ware. The later marks which incorporate the word "Casual" have been found in varying size even on identically sized pieces. Additionally, they are found in varying colors - usually pink, green or brown. Not only the re-designed ware carries this Casual mark, all pieces made late in production, even of original design, may be found with this later mark. The small code numbers contain manufacturing information which is not clear at this time. As with the earlier marks, the Casual stamped marks vary in size at random. Only the smallest Iroquois items are unmarked.

Mark 3   *Russel Wright* **CHINA** *by Iroquois*

Russel Wright **CHINA** *by Iroquois*   **Mark 4**

| Mark 5 | Mark 6 | Mark 7 | Mark 8 |

While at first there appeared to be only two Paden City-Justin Tharaud-Highlight marks, we now have found four. The PCP you will see here stands, of course, for Paden City Pottery. The fourth mark substitutes the words "Made in U.S.A." for the "Pat. Pend.". Highlight is marked in one of these ways.

| Mark 9 | Mark 10 | Mark 11 |

The number 12 Sterling mark is usually found incised, but I have heard reports of the same mark in raised relief. The number 13 mark is usually raised. Much Sterling is not marked and some of what is marked is done so imperfectly with glaze filling the words. Color will help you with these unmarked pieces. Polynesian items are back-stamped in block in a circular mark similar to the number 13 shown here. More spherically shaped, the words "Sterling China" and "Made U.S.A." surround the signature.

Mark 12

Mark 13

Identifying the Knowles line will be no problem for collectors as it is stamped with a metallic stamp and the pattern is named - mark 14.

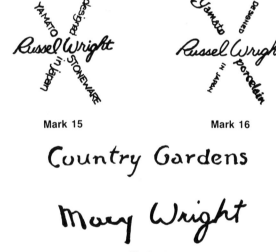

Russel Wright
by Knowles
Queen Annes Lace
MADE IN U.S.A.

Mark 14

The Yamato number 15 stoneware, porcelain number 16 and Mary Wright Country Garden number 17 marks are probably all we will find. Some Country Garden is unmarked.

Mark 15   **Mark 16**

Country Gardens

Mary Wright

Mark 17

The number 18 Oceana mark is burnt in the wood itself but a number 19 paper sticker has also been found in turquoise with white lettering.

Mark 18   *Russel Wright*

designed
by
RUSSEL
WRIGHT
"Oceana"
carved
wooden
ware
made
KLISE

Mark 19

10

Residential number 20, Flair number 21, Home Decorators number 22, all melmac lines, are as pictured here. The Meladur stamp number 23 contains the Russel Wright signature and means it is an early piece. Other Meladur, identical but without the signature, is of a later date after Wright cancelled the contract.

Mark 20

Russel Wright

RESIDENTIAL

by
Northern
BOSTON 27

Mark 21

Russel Wright

FLAIR

by
Northern
BOSTON 27
2

Mark 22

DESIGNED BY
Russel Wright
FOR
HOME DECORATORS. INC.
NEWARK
NEW YORK STATE

Mark 23

MELADUR
by
Russel Wright

PATENT APPLIED FOR

Bauer items are marked as shown in number 24, lightly incised with the signature sometimes filled with the extremely heavy glaze. Best look at possible Bauer items with a magnifying glass.

Russel Wright
BAUER

Mark 24

Yamato stoneware and porcelain companion glassware may have been paper stickered. Old Morgantown's gold paper sticker would not reproduce but the manufacturer's name is not on the sticker. Look for the signature.

The Hull stainless shown here is that made in Japan - mark number 25. That ware made by Hull in this country shows the signature, the words "Hull Stainless" and a patent number.

JAPAN HULL STAINLESS   *Russel Wright*

Mark 25

11

Imperial glassware, shown on mark number 26 was paper stickered, with black or white printing on gold background.

Mark 26

Most spun aluminum pieces are marked with the block signature shown here in number 27, but pieces also have been found with "Pat. Applied For" included. A red stamp with the Russel Wright name in block letters appears on the wooden part of some spun aluminum. Additionally a blue and white paper sticker with the designers name has surfaced. Be persistant in your search for spun aluminum by Wright. Marks are found in obscure places and the red stamp is often faint or faded. The paper stickers, of course, may have long since been washed away. A *good* sign when one looks for this is *not* to find a manufacturer's name as this ware was made from Wright's own facilities and no manufacturer's name should accompany it.

RUSSEL
WRIGHT

Mark 27

Russel Wright's chrome is believed to be unmarked.

I welcome any information you may have which adds to the number of these marks or which will add to our understanding of their significance. Please write me.

Pricing in General

The pricing information set down here comes with the usual warning that it is meant as a guide only. Rarity and regional differences will vary. Prices are for pieces in mint condition only. Neither the publisher nor the author assumes responsibility for any losses that might be incurred as a result of consulting this guide.

With those facts in mind, pricing on each line is included in each chapter. Generally, Russel Wright dinnerware collecting follows the same pattern as other collectable dinnerware. Plates, cups and saucers have found their way into early collections and there is much demand now for serving pieces, which have become more scarce and more costly. The addition of new collectors holds the flatware at its 1981 prices.

Regional differences exist but these prices are averaged from shop, show and advertising from a broad over-view of the entire country. It does not reflect the extremely high price of a city boutique, nor does it consider your neighbor's garage sale, or the sale price of a dealer who is closing shop.

As a whole, advertised items are about 25% less than shop and show prices but all have shown steady increase. If you are selling, remember that a dealer must expect a reasonable profit - something only *he* can establish. You should not expect more than 50% of these low prices if you wish to sell. If you are buying, the value of the item to your collection should be the consideration rather than this or any other guide.

Russel Wright Personal History

Russel Wright was an Ohio boy destined to search for self expression and fulfill-
ment in the market place of the whole nation. Born April 3, 1904, in Lebanon, Ohio
he could claim two signers of the Declaration of Independence as forebearers.
His father was a local judge in Lebanon and with such a background, it seems
certain that his stock was sturdy and the work-ethic ingrained by birth. Without
a doubt, his artistic disposition, a rare combination of artistic genius and a tireless
dogged determination resulted in his success. At the age of 17, with a part time
job in a munitions factory, he spent his Saturday afternoons in painting classes
at the Cincinnati Art Academy with Frank Duveneck. After graduation, he entered
Princeton University to study law, but also attended the Columbia School of Architecture. Already he had won the first and second Tiffany prizes for the most
outstanding war memorial of 1920. At Princeton, his law courses suffered from
neglect as he found himself interested and involved in set and production work
for the Triangle Shows. Having attracted the attention of Norman Bel Geddes
he felt there was a place for him in the artistic world. His legal studies came to
a halt while he spent his time in stage and costume design. This field was to be
rewarding, for he was to work with the Theatre Guild and later design sets fo
several New York productions. He had his own workshop where theatrical properties were produced and in this happy period he met and married Mary Einstein, a talented designer. She became one of the major contributors to his success, working tirelessly to promote her husband and his work. Together they produced and sold the now sought-after miniature animals to New York boutiques
catering to the wealthy.

By 1930, New York department stores were asking for copies of his stage furniture and accessories and the theatrical part of his life was closed out as more
orders came and the need for backstock in accessories grew. The commission
part of his work, still sold largely to the wealthy, was to taper and beginning with
spun aluminum, he began to design for the great body of Americans to whom
we often apply the term "every man", the middle-class American. He established
his own small factory and design firm, setting out to produce the first metal informal serving pieces in New York City. His spun aluminum was to lead to national
distribution as orders came in from all across the country. He was directly responsible for beginning the move to design home furnishings geared to informal living
and entertaining.

During this spun aluminum period, the Wrights met Irving Richards, who operate
a very successful shop in New York City. Richards joined forces with the Wright
in the business side of Russel Wright Inc., renamed Russel Wright Accessories
They believed in the future of colorful, functional good design. The seeds of Wright'
American Modern were growing. The unique Raymor Company evolved from thi
business arrangement and the Wright's own experience in manufacturing and me
chandising contributed to its successful growth. Raymor became a leader in th
marketing field and was recognized as a leader in the field of the excellent, th
new and the different. With coordinated avant-garde merchandise, they enlarge
the giftware market to include large department stores, meeting a greatly expanded
market.

In 1939 while studying, now at New York University School of Architecture, and with many national companies as clients, he was finally able to convince The Steubenville Pottery Company to produce his first dinnerware - American Modern. This came after many rejections and then only because the Wrights would guarantee production costs. A departure from all that came before, it was to be an enormous accomplishment design-wise and marketing-wise. The designer was launched on a path of success with areas so diverse that it is impossible to name all the items he designed. None were to bring him more acceptance than his tabletop fashions, however. The Steubenville experiment gloriously rewarded Russel Wright with many other dinnerware and related accounts. He was able to establish himself as an acknowledged leader in the group of American designers who were striving for excellence in a modern manner.

It is important to our understanding at this time to know that Wright agreed to design exclusively for Raymor for a five-year period. So fundamentally necessary was this business alliance between the Wrights and Richards, that it was an all or nothing gamble with the future of his design business at risk. In summary then, the house of cards built first on the American Modern dinnerware depended on the Wrights financing to the Steubenville pottery and the marketing first done under Russel Wright Associates and then by the newly formed Richards-Wright distribution firm of Raymor. In an effort to accomplish good results in these areas, all Wright design work in the field of home furnishings was to be marketed by Raymor for this five year period. Of course, the gamble paid. More American Modern was produced and sold than any other dinnerware before or since. It has become a marketing classic and won the American Designers Institute Award for the best ceramic design of 1941. Many awards were to follow - none more significantly important to his career.

At this point, I believe we should examine the basic philosophy which inspired Russel Wright. A longer look at the concentrated means by which he was able to promote his dreams and dishes seems in order also.

Later biographers have described Russel Wright's work as having been influenced by this school, that movement, or another. Each, it seems, has tried to discover a new or fresh adjective with which to pin down the Wright style. It is this writer's belief that the designer drew freely from any and all domestic and foreign art and design movements as it pleased him to do so. His work certainly has traces of work done by his contemporaries in art, but he borrowed only those traces which helped him define his own statement, rejecting whole-scale formulas of others as being too restrictive and not evolving out of the needs of a changed world, but merely reflecting it. Call it what you will, *he* called it American Modern (his philosophy, as well as his products.) He said it should ''spring from native sources. Reflections such as Classic Modern, Neo Classic, only tend to disturb the true course of modern in this country and are not acceptable because their decadent sophistication renders such styles unpalatable to the average American consumer. I feel that American Colonial design furnishes us with a healthy native tradition - a solid foundation for the continuance of creditable American design.'' In his opinion, the aim of modern design should be to reject the traditional, however disguised with some new name.

Russel Wright had arrived at this statement by an evolutionary process, of course. ''We were impressed with the way the originators of the Bauhaus cleaned the slate to create their own style. We wanted to do the same instead of reviving one period after another - French, English, or even that ridiculous Art Deco, which is nothing more than a corny revision of cubism." Moving past the Bauhaus, however, he stated "It was too austere and inhuman. In 1934 I broke away from what I call my T-square and triangle period to design a more human chair for the Museum of Modern Art." Beautiful design artistically treated, embodied in a functional shape, made affordable to the masses, sums up simplistically what Russel Wright designs are all about.

His was a commitment to excellence and quality whatever the cost. Strict adherence to his social concept was primary. To create the widest possible market at the lowest possible cost became his personal formula in his work as he applied his philosophy to the divergent personal needs of "every man". He had worked for the elite few and had now turned his back on them as style leaders. He looked instead to the huge body of people of more average means, who he felt should have good design made available to them in the form of everyday items. They were to be the benefactors of his philosophy and easier living was to be theirs. The best things in life should be almost free - or at least, sell for a reasonable price.

A slowly evolving influence in his work was the Oriental classic form. Almost from the beginning, one sees the adaptation of the Eastern accent used increasingly and consistantly. The Eastern and Native American were both primary to his work as it evolved and they remained central in his work for over thirty years.

The first spun aluminum, the first solid wood furniture of modern design, the first aluminum blinds, the first informal serving accessories, the first stainless steel flatware, the first sectional furniture, the first indestructible dinnerware only lead the parade of his work to support his conviction that "good design is for everyone." An "ism" was developing. As he identified with the average consumer, we identified with him, and his personal crusade found many who espoused his cause as well as his wares.

Spreading the gospel became a business ritual also. Having already established himself with Raymor, and having achieved some success in manufacturing and marketing under the Wright's Accessories Company, which still operated as his design firm, certain contractual and merchandising programs became standard. Everyone got the same standard contract with the same stipulations, except in special circumstances. Generally, Wright was to receive 5% on goods sold a lesser amount on second quality. This was to continue until sales dipped to a specified figure, after which both parties dissolved the agreement and the designs reverted to the designer. The manufacturer was to assume advertising costs but was free to use the Russel Wright signature (in most cases) providing it appeared in print larger than any other print on the page. It is mind-boggling to review the designer's correspondence to police these details. He repeatedly wrote to clients over any variance with the agreement and his constant checking on the agreement was proof that there was more than a measure of the businessman here. No detail, either artistic or business was too small for his attention and it was his strong hold on practical concerns that permitted the concessions he made to customers. If any part of his lines met customer resistance, if salesmen reported general slumps, contractually he agreed to restyle the line or redesign items. If the need for an additional item seemed wise, he did that design. Out of this clause came two terms which we should define and describe as they apply to his designs

The first, "experimental item" must be a broader concept than we usually regard it. Usually we equate experimental as "first" or "early", but when one considers the contractural agreements described, it becomes clear that experimentation, trial and error were continuing components in all the lines. An original piece found lacking might be re-designed and still be found unpopular. Experiments in Russel Wright designs began early but remained as possiblities as long as the line was in production.

The term "prototype" needs explanation also, as it describes a broader number of items than the name suggests. It does not mean "one of a kind", as we often consider it. In the Russel Wright lines, it may mean a "short run" involving enough ware to be shown at various sales promotions to the trade - with the rest of the run being left to a company's research and development departments. Prototypes did make their way into collections even though they were not marketed. Someone found a use for them, and usually some found their way out of the sales rooms and into collections.

Both Russel and Mary made themselves available for personal appearances, store openings and public gatherings. Stores might be selling his dinnerware, but the Wrights were selling the Russel Wright name, and there seemed no end to the lengths to which they would go. Slide programs which illustrated proper usages were presented across the country as Russel and Mary could be seen putting beef and beans on various colored plates, illustrating their point that color selection *was* important. (Charcoal, he pointed out, was best.) Orchestrating it all beautifully, they catapulted a designer's name as an endorsement of quality, so recognized as good merchandising today, but another first for Russel and Mary.

Of course it worked phenomenally. His name quickly had a "brand value" and was listed alongside that of manufacturers, but larger, and we looked for the name as we shopped. A national campaign to promote Wright designs evolved with awareness directed at the manufacturer, retailer and consumer. Customers were told that Nelson Rockefeller used American Modern. "Imagine *that*, I use it too!" was the amazed response of a laborer working on Wright's new house. Statistics showed that young white collar people were its chief enthusiasts and magazine surveys showed recognition many times over older more established names. Gimbel's was the scene of a near riot in 1946 as the result of a 2" x 4" newspaper ad. When the store opened, a block long queue had formed. Several people were hurt during a rush that was estimated as a constant 100 customers per sales person. Hundreds of orders were written for which there was no stock. In large department stores such as Altman's, Bloomingdales and Gimbels in New York as well as J.L. Hudson in Detroit crowds gathered and it was necessary to establish a supermarket technique to handle the sale of Wright Dinnerware. Hudson's orders were shipped in by the boxcar. In Baltimore, Smitty's Fish Market received a carload of "seconds" three or four times a year; ware was sold directly from the railroad car with crowds so large that police were necessary to control them. In Middletown, New York, there was a Russel Wright Club - composed of bridge players whose prizes were confined to articles of Russel Wright design. It was a wonderful time for the Wrights.

In the meantime, museums, schools and foundations were awarding medals, prizes and honors to the various products. Wright had surrounded himself with a few top quality associates, most of whom were responsible for production and business details, and his own design office was overwhelmed with client prospects. In 1941, the designer originated a new merchandising program called the "American Way". This was a collective group of artists, artisans and designers who would contribute their work to collections two times a year. Manufacturers were to work closely with them, and a resultant juried collection which was embodied with the Wright philosophy and marketed with his expertise was to have evolved. The contributors, forty in number, boasted the names of some of the leading designers of the day. In theory the "Way" was to encourage artisans and craftsmen to design certain articles compatible with the new American look, resulting in increased sales. An elaborate sales system evolved. Department stores featured exhibit rooms where the complimentary nature of all the products could be seen and customers were urged to use them as guides and select items to fit their own needs. The large group of designers soon became unwieldy and distribution problems, as well as a deficiency in quality control resulted. It was abandoned after two years, although it would have encouraged fresh young talent and would have added a new dimension to hand and machine made products. It was a Wright adaptation of the Arts and Crafts movement restated and ill fated. Overseeing so many artists in this large scale endeavor was probably more than Russel could find time for - and it was not likely he would have let anyone else put his endorsement on work he'd not personally approved. Wright had financed the program and it took ten years to pay his obligations.

In 1951 Russel and Mary wrote *A Guide to Easier Living* which aimed at efficient housekeeping and rewarding leisure through the application of business practices and motion management in the home. It was much like a plan devised by an efficiency expert on how to organize one's housekeeping. Outlining a plan for living and arranging the work in a home from the design of a house down to the smallest details on how to entertain with ease, the book was a bestseller and is sought after today. In my own experience, it was a woman killer! Such single mindedness over housework is seldom found and the attention to detail so minute that *this* housekeeper never even got to the chapters on how to enjoy one's leisure. At the same time, those who followed his "ism" lived by it for some time. We were a text book oriented generation. We established housekeeping according to *Guide for Easier Living*. We read Gilbreath's *Cheaper By the Dozen* and we raised our children according to Dr. Spock. In a changing world, our parent's way of doing things had passed and we looked to new experts to point the new way. Many of these idols were to fall as authorities, of course, but we lived with their proposals for a time and it seemed to make sense to us then, in spite of the rigors of the practice it worked on us.

Russel Wright became the President of the Society of Industrial Designers in 1951, adding to his huge collection of honors. It must have been personally rewarding to be so honored by his peers.

Looking backward, Russel Wright's life, his philosophy and the great body of his work seem to have many contradictions and seem ever to be in contradiction to each other. With a few facts in mind and with charitable respect for the man as a person as well as a designer, the whole can be seen as congruous.

As stated, we must always be aware of the important fact that his self perception was different from actuality. He saw himself as a social critic with a philosophy which had at its core the concern for the large middle classes. His great talents were, he believed, devoted to enriching the lives of that group, but he accomplished that by much personal suffering and was unable to adapt his philosophy to his own life. He had never been a part of any group himself. His work was his passion and his artistic talents found release there. In spite of disclaiming an interest in commerce, there is ample evidence that he enjoyed the market place. He was an opportunist with no negative connotations. He seized opportunities and ideas with equal fervor.

The market place may have been the area which, by giving him acceptance, made his personal life acceptable to him. He had never become a real member of the family he had married into. He had never taken on the protective coloration of New York, and perhaps his rejection of the values of the wealthy social group there accounted for the fact that he never made a place for himself in that group. He was not urbane nor socially polished. High society ignored him as a person while they furnished their homes with his designs. The long continued friendship/work relationships which he enjoyed with Herbert Honig and Irving Richards are in contradiction to most of his experiences. Herbert Honig, as business manager, took charge of the coordination of business details so diverse that only one who was a personal friend (and mind reader) could have maintained order. Until this time (1950), Russel had been too involved with details of commerce, he believed, and it was with great relief that he turned over the details to his friend. Richards proved to be a good friend with a good sense of intuition, knowledgeable insights and a willingness to deal with Russel as he found him. These friendships had to have been very important to Russel and spanned many years.

The accusation of being too commercial was leveled at him by other designers of his day. The large body of his productivity set him apart from this fraternity and his peers considered him as too profit-oriented to be a serious designer. He had a bad reputation with this group who believed him to be a "gate crasher" in their midst.

He was said to be complex and difficult - and he was. The groups from which he held himself apart reflected his feelings about them and he was considered to be an outsider, out of place in every group but with those whose cause he championed. His life then was a revolt. Iconoclastic and complicated, there seemed to be no "niche" into which he could find ease. He never felt "at home" with his surroundings and even in his best times, he identified with earlier Depression days, and with the people for whom he designed. In so doing, he championed not only us, but himself. His was a variable disposition, hard to forecast and seldom serene. His own unrest and dissatisfactions may, however, account for his doggedness in pursuing his high standards. Things *did* make a difference to him and his better nature—his philosophy as well as his great talent—were openly exposed to all who bought his wares. No other designer's work contained more of a personal message than did his. A rebel with a cause, he often achieved different results for the sake of being different. Even thumbing his nose at his designer contemporaries gave him small pleasure, however. His personal lot was a hard one.

The rejection that came his way in the later lines we will discuss was taken as a personal blow and since his buyers had been his appreciative audience, the blows hurt. Bitterness resulted and he became a petulant law unto himself. Others, he felt, capitalized on his work. He had never "kept up" with any aspect of life except as it touched his work. To find his work failing made him withdraw even from that and in 1968, he closed his studio.

With his expertise, he became involved with the Department of State in 1955 as an advisor for eastern countries on ways to improve their handicrafts for export. He worked in Japan with factories there on product development and set up handicraft centers in Taiwan and Vietnam. He was re-emphasizing his creed internationally. Small wonder that in 1965, he was invited back to Japan to do design work for more than a hundred firms. In his last years, he parlayed some work with the Johnston Park Beautification Program into a new adventure - into an association with the National Park system and was closely identified with public lands and their reclamation and continued use by the public.

The rebel retreated at last to his own project - his property at Garrison, New York, and had long since put his tap roots there. He and Mary had bought 80 acres in 1941, using it first as a week-end retreat and finally moving into a small house. During his later years, he personally cleared much of his land on weekends—chopping, cutting, burning brush. He said, "I go back to New York on Monday physically exhausted but greatly stimulated and what I'd learned on Saturday and Sunday began to show up unconsciously in my regular work". I offer his Garrison experiences as an alternative answer to the burning question of "Did he compromise his designs in the end?" I think not. I believed he had matured and some of his new interests became part of his work. Admittedly, he had espoused minimalism and decried decoration, but his later incorporation of it was so tastefully executed that it should not offend even the purist. Had he compromised, were his later works a "sell out", it would have meant a rejection of his own basically perceived personality, a disavowal of his own philosophy and these later designs would probably have not been the commercial failures they were. With his great talents, a compromise could have been achieved which would have duplicated his former successes. To the point, it seems, is the fact that the consumer had changed, and he had been unable to change with him and intuitive as he was, he had simply misread the taste, time and needs of the newer group of homemakers. His reach had exceeded his grasp - not an unusual state of affairs.

The retreat to Dragon Rock and the house he built there opened even new vistas for he indulged himself, building an exaggerated, impractical, breathtakingly beautiful "part-pavillion, part-cave" home on the walls of an abandoned quarry. Actually hewn from rock are the walls, floors and steps with glass walls overlooking the outcropping stone from the quarry and the magnificent waterfall he contrived. The inside is an extention of the outside. It is literally a "temple of earthly delight" with constant surprises - the fireplace literally "comes in" from the exterior rock formation. A bathtub with stone masonry imitates the waterfall with the jewel of a pool at its base. The walls, painted a forest green, have hemlock needles pressed in them uniting themselves with the hemlock grove across the way. Butterflies and ferns are embedded in panels and sliding doors. Wild flowers grow in pockets along the steps which lead to the lower level and a tree grows from the bottom to the top of the house. One feels as though there is no demarcation between inside and outside and the illusion had to have been even greater while he lived there for rya rugs resembling pads of moss covered areas of the stone floors. The acreage itself was turned into nature trails where naturalistic beauty grows with carefully controlled abandon. Wild flowers and a four-acre Laurel

field relieve the sterness of the jagged quarry cliffs with its huge stern rock formation. Long a champion of the home as being one's refuge, this was his and there
can be no doubt that here he may have found the peace and tranquility he'd not
found before. Obviously to his critics, this was no home to which *A Guide to Easier
Living* could be applied in total, but was the life-styled home he wanted. Caring
for it was left to others. This was his gift to himself. It is the ultimate in Russel
Wright, and if you would know more, you'll find it pictured in the March 16, 1962,
edition of *Life* magazine. He gave the grounds to the Nature Conservancy and
worked with them to reclaim nature trails and flower walks, pruning judiciously
and creating a center for the appreciation of nature. Often asked how he found
such a beautiful site, Wright's answer was that he recognized the potential and
had set nature into a delicate harmonious balance. What seems so natural was
contrived.

He died December 23, 1976, of a heart attack and missed the second-time
around phenomena of his designs. If his long range thinking had led him to expect this renewed interest in his work, he would have advertised it all as "tomorrow's collectable." It's double life surpasses the double duty he so often pointed
out and his faith in us, and in himself, would have been renewed.

In retrospect, Russel Wright touched our lives as few do. He has given us a
new respect for ourselves as Americans. With an art that concealed art, he brought
beauty to the things we used every day and our appreciation of them reinforced
our dignity. We were elevated. To paraphrase him, he had appealed to our national self-respect and individual self-confidence. He had relieved the sameness
in our lives and the changes were permanent. Some of us still practice bits and
pieces of his philosophy, giving credit to Russel and Mary.

Many of us packed the dishes away for a while, certain they were important
and his creed remained as part of our lives. We would never be the same. If you're
just now meeting Russel Wright in your new collecting, welcome to the group.
Our numbers have been many from the beginning and your enthusiasm in the
re-discovering of his work does honor to his memory. I invite you to write me. Each
new find adds to the pleasure of the company.

The Spun Aluminum Adventure

Russel Wright is said to have taken aluminum out of the kitchen, styled it in a modern manner and then returned it in forms and shapes utilitarian and decorative. His extensive use of the material covered about a ten-year time span, with the forced abandonment caused by the war and the curtailment of the aluminum usage except in war efforts.

Early in the 1930's, Wright's career needed direction if he was to be the beacon light of design he hoped to be. He had served a sort of apprenticeship with his sales of animals and pewter pieces to the wealthy and in a speech he prepared later he stated that in 1929, "The idea of acquiring clients or working for a large producer or factory seemed so impossible that we gave little thought to it." The age of the industrial designer had not yet arrived but spun aluminum was to be the designer's journey into that bigger world.

In 1930, Russel and Mary, living in a coach house in New York City, were able to combine their efforts, use the ground floor of their living quarters as a manufacturing area, and launch Russel Wright Incorporated as a unit with design, manufacturing and marketing capabilities, concentrating on the new metal.

The permanency of chromium plating and stainless steel made it desirable but electroplating was expensive and tooling and fabrication even higher. Aluminum, still comparably inexpensive and easy to work with, was an exciting alternative for a young designer who wanted to design *everything* and who had only a small vacant area and a work bench. The addition of a spinning lathe made manufacturing of spun aluminum pieces possible and Wright quickly found himself established as a leading designer, having pioneered with this new usage of aluminum. Aluminum Company of America soon sent their people to observe his use of this new medium and they entered the market with their new Kennsington Company. The Wright lines were the uncontested leaders, however, and they brought other manufacturers of many other types of products to his doors, many of whom were to become design clients.

The properties of aluminum, ease of workability, and its permanent integral color made for production ease. Russel, inspired by it, was free to follow his inspiration as a designer in an unchartered area, and Mary, with her real capabilities, was to attend to the business details involved in the marketing. As the line developed, Wright's style developed and out of these early experiences, the Wrights were also to develop design and merchandising principles which would become fundamental in their later works. Coming at a time when there was nothing on the market between paper plates and gold embossed china, the spun aluminum experience was a significant step in the home furnishings field and equally significant to the Wrights in that it established Wright as a designer of first-rate importance. The early business experiences were to be refined later but became invaluable lessons learned early.

In a short two years, Mary found herself making store demonstrations, organizing and executing sales coordination, composing advertisements (free to customers), as well as overseeing the actual production. Mushrooming as the business was, the Wrights realized early that the expertise of a distributor was needed and in 1932, Mary Ryan was called in to serve that need, which she did until Russel joined forces with Irving Richards. Spun aluminum was one of the first products to be handled later by Raymor.

The slightly exaggerated forms of the new spun aluminum, modern in every sense, were typical of forms used later in ceramics. Spherical shapes, circular lines, were limited only by the quality of metal and its workability. The resultant pieces were new in style as well as material. Although extreme, they were well accepted by homemakers who found them modern in concept but not so extreme as Deco designs which had proven hard to adapt to already owned furnishings. These new items further seemed to serve a new purpose for which we were only beginning to see a need. Changing modes of entertaining, the trend being toward large informal affairs, called for new items with interchangeable uses. These new aluminum pieces, colorless and pleasingly shaped, light weight and often oversized, blended well with older serving items. The use of several types of wood, ceramics, glass, cane, cork and rattan made for interesting combinations and added informality to the plain material.

It all started with a cheese board! That was the original item produced and for a long period of time, the Wrights felt they could never make enough cheese boards or enough variations of them. All were sold as fast as produced. Americans and the Wrights had discovered cheese to be a favorite food for the new informal entertaining event - the cocktail party. What had begun with the cheese board quickly fell into three categories: stove to table ware, informal serving accessories, and interior accessories which included book ends, smoking materials, lamps and the like. All three lines were readily accepted, the designer was flooded with orders and new additions were made as rapidly as Russel could design them and Mary could produce and ship them. A huge line developed—some more elaborate and some very basic—but most incorporating glass, ceramic, wood, cork, cane or rattan in various ways.

From the first, this new line was conceived as "open stock" with interchangeable usage, but the ensemble concept was promoted and used successfully - a good lesson for what was to follow. A "Sixtette" group was offered with the six items selling for $10.95 - a savings to the customer. Since this reduced the retailer's profit (while enlarging the designers), retailers were given a sixty cents refund on all Sixtette sales to guarantee their mark up. Sixtettes sold as did sets called "Sunday Supper, Beer Buffet, Cocktail Hour, Midnight Snack, Popcorn Picnic, Sunday Breakfast, After Bridge." Mary's concepts, these groupings were put to test early and were basic to later policies. The customer was told that plain steel wool rubbed in the direction of the grooving would erase scratching and keep the aluminum bright. That it dented easily and bent alarmingly was not mentioned.

Actually hundreds of items were produced - ice buckets, casseroles with ceramic inserts, fruit bowls, lamps, ash trays, cannister sets, bun warmers, vases and serving items of every variety. The list goes on and on and seemed to end only when the war ended it. During those few years, an amazing number of various items were offered and sold rapidly. Each piece had many variations. Many markings have been found on the aluminum but the interesting fact is that the signature was not yet being used. The name appears in block letters, most often simply Russel Wright on the bottom of the item. On some covered pieces, the mark may be on the underside of the lid. A red-inked stamp is sometimes found on the wood and I have seen a navy and white paper label, suggesting that there may be some umarked spun aluminum which is label-less. On some of the cheese boards, the name is followed by "Pat. applied for" which leaves us wondering if Wright was attempting to patent the idea or the item. I have not heard from the U.S. Patent Office on this.

Two pieces are especially interesting and need explanation. The Samovar and coffee urn was a piece custom designed for Emaline Johnston of the pharmaceutical family. It was a modern adaptation of the old Russian samovar and well insulated to protect furniture. It brewed fifty cups of coffee (by means of a "scientific percolator contraption") or thirty cups of tea, and did so quickly. The adaptation of the sphere in his design is seen here. The Bain Marie was originally custom designed for a member of the Vanderbilt family and came with or without a base which could be used as a buffet-table griddle. Both of these pieces were dated about 1935 and the work on both was so complicated that they were manufactured by outside facilities and not in the Wright's coach-house factory. I am unable to picture a buffet-table popcorn popper or the spaghetti set which were other large and interesting items. These were "show pieces." Many smaller, less expensive, less complicated items which constituted the large production interest collectors today.

The spun aluminum line produced was enlarged to include a heavier grade aluminum named *Platene*. You will find it to have a more molded rotund shaping and its amorphous styling will set it apart from the rest of the spun aluminum work. It is different. It is *Platene,* signed with the designer's name and sold in the mid-1930's by Russel Wright Accessories.

These 1930-1943 years can be described as the "Age of Metal in Design." In a way that was to be his custom, Russel Wright was early on the scene, prolific in offerings and accepted by those who would enter the changing world of entertaining.

On Pricing Spun Aluminum

It is difficult to present actual values for the many different spun aluminum pieces as not only were there many variations but the collecting of it is still relatively new. The figures I can offer must be adjusted to relate to the complexity of the item as well as the number of component parts it may possess. Shop prices begin a about $25.00 and reach as much as $125.00 at the present. These figures, o course, do not apply to large custom-designed pieces, such as the Samovar, Pop corn Popper and Bain Marie, nor do they apply to badly scratched or dented pieces. Although the Bain Marie usually leaked and the popcorn popper would not pop on occasions seems not to have affected their desirability for collectors. I expec all spun aluminum to be more expensive in the future as collectors complete din nerware "sets" and seek to add to their Russel Wright collections by acquiring items other than ceramic. Spun aluminum is a "good buy" for the present bu we should expect higher prices in the future.

#124 Two tier Tid Bit; #192 Cork ball tray; #470 9″ casserole walnut handles
Pottery insert; #909 Gravy set. Hand carved, walnut handle. Copy of an early
pewter set; #138 Ice pail 6½″, slotted wood spoon for ice cubes. Available
in three sizes; #1000 Sandwich humidor.

#823 Candelabra 18″ x 4″; #139 vegetable set; #530 ice bucket and tongs #367 Lemonade set; #98 cheese board and cover; American Modern plates Stainless steel. Linen, lemonade beakers and ball shakers not Wright designs

New Year's Table Shows Spun Aluminum; #124 sandwich humidor; #124 two tiered tid-bit; #333 bun warmer.

#432 Samovar 17″, capacity 2¼ gallons. From the collection of Paul Walters.

#367 Lemonade Pitcher; Coffee Pot; After dinner cup with porcelain insert. Note: Lemonade pitcher sold in set. Inserts not believed to be Wright design.

#110 Large Relish Rosette; #330 Bun Warmer; #124 Tea Set; #907 Nestin
Bowls, Available 10″, 9″, 7″. Sold as unit or separately; Ball Vase, 10½″
Muffin warmer.

The Chromium Look

Very early in his working life, Russel Wright recognized the clean sharp beauty of chrome, popular in the Deco period and for some years after. Only the difficulty of fabrication of the metal prevented him from the use of it in his small manufacturing/coach house area, but as early as 1933, some of the most striking chromium pieces on the market had been conceived in that work place. Their numbers are few, but each embodies the freshness of spirit which the chrome itself stood for. Would it replace silver in home usage? Often asked, the reply had to be with the young, artistically oriented group who had already put silver "in its place". The cylindrical fish aquarium 20″ long and 5½″ high with chrome ends was (and remains) enough to entice one to go out and buy fish. A hanging ball-shaped aquarium 8″ wide caught almost as much attention; electrical heater units for both were available. Double coil book ends, high on one side, low on the other, were made and some early work on legs for a bar stool was done. The spherical theme to which the designer often returned was first presented in a Saturn vase, 8″ x 11″, round, with a flower arranger top. Advertisements for these early items do not name the manufacturer.

Wright signed a contract with The Chase Chromium and Brass Company of New York in the mid 1930's. Chase, the acknowledged leader in the industry, freely used the best designers of its time and a roster of its designers is almost a "Who's Who." Having made a solid reputation during the Deco period, the company did not use designers' names on the works they designed, but sales literature did give credits due. Therein is our identity problem with the ten items Russel Wright contracted to do for them in 1936. None are marked with the Wright signature. Some few items are known to be his—an ice pail, a beer pitcher, and a handsome corn set were all offered in the 1936 catalogue. His ten-year association with Chase however, leaves the collector speculating on the other seven items. It must be remembered that working concerns of those years never guessed that their records were to become source material for researchers and scholars. The lack of supportive evidence in Chase papers and the absence of reference to specific items in the Syracuse papers leaves us dissatisfied with our lack of a concrete listing of these chrome items.

There is much speculation, however, on the missing items, and those who try to identify them have reasonable grounds for their opinions. The spherical theme used in the corn set shakers was also used in Chase sugar shakers, large salt & peppers and the like, and one could make a logical assumption that these also may be Wright designs. Other sets than the corn set used the small blue glass tray and it seems reasonable that these too may be his designs. All is speculative at this time.

The corn set stands out as a favorite item in any Russel Wright collection. The small 6″ blue glass tray held a tiny 5½″ oil can spouted pitcher for butter (or cream or salad dressing or chocolate sauce) and was accompanied by spheres 1¾″ and 1⅛″. These are frequently found in parts, their whole having been broken over the years and some collectors own a "mini-set" of Chase which they are trying to complete. The ice bowl and tongs are 7″ across and large enough to contain snacks with the tong handle becoming the handle for the ice bowl turned snack server.

Wright's long association with Chase seemed untroubled and reflects the experience Chase had working with the designers. Firm contractual agreements were made early and each party knew exactly what his rights were. It is the collector's loss that we can offer no more definite details at this time.

On Pricing Chromium

A Russel Wright collector must recognize that Chase Chrome is a collectable in its own right today and so do not be surprised at its high value. At the same time, the Russel Wright snydrome is so epidemic that his designs are the most sought after of the Chase pieces. There are no bargains in this area of our interest and prices asked vary from $50.00 to $125.00 with the corn set and its components at the top end of that scale. ''Could-be'' items should be priced more modestly but a Chase piece of simple design by an unknown designer is still expensive.

And Also Wood

With a life span time which paralleled the early years of the spun aluminum ware, Russel Wright's Oceana line's performance bears little else in common with the aluminum, notwithstanding the interesting usage of the two together.

Oceana was made by The Klise Woodenware Company of Grand Rapids, Michigan, in 1935, and took its name from the marine motif which inspired the various serving pieces. Machine-made of either hazelwood with its dark brown grain or of Wright's own favorite, blonde maple, the pieces have the appearance of hand-sculptured wood. The free form combined with the wood grain no doubt contribute to this illusion. Only a relatively small line evolved, and one can suppose that if it had met with more success, would have become the nucleus for much more—as occurred with other products.

Conceived about the same time as American Modern, Oceana was to be shown with it later. But even the best selling dinnerware could not promote its tag-along companion. The reasons for its lack of popularity are obscure, evading even Wright Associates who were particularly impressed with Oceana. Perhaps the seeds of its failure were in the fact that it was theme-oriented and so limited the numbers of buyers to whom it appealed. Other lines were to have much broader concepts, multiple uses for many occasions, and feature the developed Wright creed. This early line, interesting as it is, can be called an early marketing failure. It has been said that the centerpiece bowl was the most sculpturally beautiful of all the items, most of which drew upon shells and sea plants for their inspiration. These, treated abstractly, comprised the Oceana theme. Available were:

Shell candy box 3″ x 9″, starfish relish 13½″, snail relish 10″, nut bowl 2″ x 5″, wing shell bread tray 6″, buella shell bowl for fruit or salad 13″ x 18″, fluted salad bowl 4½″ x 9″, seaweed relish tray 4½″ x 19″, combination serving tray or salad bowl 10″ x 18″, lazy susan 15″, flat shell salad bowl 12″, snail salt, hostess tray with four nappies 11″ x 24″, wave salad bowl in three sizes, 4″ x 13″, 3½″ x 10½″ and 3″ x 9″. Reversible relish rosette with one side for relish usage and the other as cheese and cracker board 14″, one handled server for canapes and snacks 6¼″ x 17½″, pearl shell plate 9″.

Signature marks in burnt wood have been found; turquoise paper stickers are also known to exist.

Had Oceana been the popular line hoped for, it would have been one of Russel Wright's contributions to his American Way program. Both the concepts were to be abandoned early however, and even Raymor's efforts were not enough to rescue Oceana.

An additional wooden line, dating from the mid-1950's, has been pictured in what appears to be limited advertising. Simple rectangular or square shapes said to have been inspired by American Indian chopping bowls are identity features. Probably marked as Oceana with a burnt signature, none has come to my attention.

Both wooden lines must be considered very rare.

On Pricing Oceana

So little of this Klise woodenware was sold, so little seen today, that it is impossible to give you approximate values with any real basis. Be aware that rarity effects values and that may help you with pricing. Few Russel Wright collections contain Oceana, and as it is so attractive, it should not remain long at a shop or show.

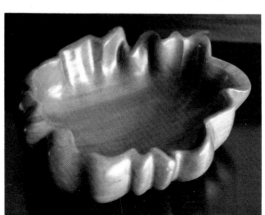

Wave salad bowl; snail relish dish; fluted salad bowl.

Oceana hostess tray shown here by courtesy of The Brooklyn Museum. Gift of Arthur Drummond.

American Modern and Oceana.

33

American Modern Dinnerware

The timeliness of American Modern's entrance in the dinnerware scene may very well be one of the reasons for its almost instant popularity. It was 1939 and the world news was not good news. War and our involvement seemed imminent, and as a nation we were anxious to forget that fact and eagerly sought ways to reaffirm our hopes that our just-found prosperity would bring us to the "good life".

Russel Wright was able to contribute to our sense of tranquility with his philosophy and his confirmation that our homes and furnishings were of prime importance. A measure of patriotism and a return to the home as the center of our well-being were no doubt worthy goals and if Russel Wright and his designs reinforced those goals, the homemaker of those troubled times was overwhelmingly pleased to follow his lead.

The success of his recoloring and reshaping of the American pottery market had been preceeded by his spun-aluminum, radios, lamps and more. Departures from the traditional, they met with instant success, possibly resulting from the fact that they could be mass-produced, and therefore were well-designed items within the financial reach of most people. The designer, then, with some confidence, turned his talents to what was to be his greatest design accomplishment - American Modern dinnerware.

Combining the new modern influence with classic American primitive lines, American Modern embodied all that the designer had been trying to actuate in his other work. American consumers, in numbers never before or since, adopted the philosophy and the dishes. Depression-programmed, we admired its "less-is-better" look. Mamie Eisenhower was said to have used it as her "everyday" dishes, following the example of Eleanor Roosevelt's endorsement of Wright's work.

Customer approval was rewarding to the designer in all ways, for this dinnerware had been a difficult problem for him. It met with consistent non-approval from the pottery industry itself. Strongly conservative (to the end), the great potteries of the Ohio River area all agreed that it was radical, harsh, costly to produce, an uncertain gamble, and one by one they refused to manufacture it. That from the time of its production - 1939-1959, it went on to gross $150,000,000 in sales and became the largest selling dinnerware ever in the history of pottery sales was due to the designer's confidence - and his money.

In a last gamble for its own solvency, the Steubenville Pottery in Steubenville, Ohio, agreed to go into production with Mary and Russel Wright's agreement to finance the production. A large account, J. L. Hudson's in Detroit, had made a personal request for its production - a favorable sign. Sold at first through Russel Wright Accessories, Raymor would soon distribute it exclusively for five years. After that time, Wright sold his Raymor stock, drawing royalties from Raymor instead. By 1939, both the distributor and Russel Wright had time-tested sales techniques and a massive nationwide advertising campaign in operation. Sixteen-piece starter sets were available as were 53-piece sets. Open stock, a new concept, made additions to a set easily obtainable. One could buy now and add later.

An effort was made to break the set into smaller groupings so that one would be encouraged to complete smaller sets as well as a dinnerware set. Suggested pieces formed a "Child's group - under 3" "Child's group 3-5" (these child's groups were boxed and sold as such in 1953), "Everyday group", "Buffet group"

"Barbecue or Patio group", "Television group", and "Bridge group". Surely, if you were pleased with your already-owned dinnerware, you must need a "group" of some sort! All pieces used for cooking were said to be oven-proof (Don't take that test). If all else failed to win purchasers, you were reminded that serving pieces were so interesting that they made desirable gifts when purchased individually. It all worked, for our direction in living and entertaining had changed. There was a shift away from the dining room as the place to eat, and we now found ourselves eating all over the house. Buffets, brunches and cocktail parties replaced luncheons, teas and formal dinner parties. Television contributed to changes, and we now ate in front of "the set". The family room replaced the kitchen. We needed new items for new uses. Wright had recognized trends early and American Modern pioneered in meeting our new needs.

No one who could read could overlook American Modern dinnerware, and it was unlikely to be missed by even those who didn't read, for pictures of the new pieces were eye-assaulting and prolific with the designer's signature always present. Mass produced for the middle-income group, American Modern was widely advertised in the mass media of the day and the best known department stores in the country placed full-page ads in all the leading magazines. It was a revolution in the pottery industry and a sales phenomena in the retail business.

Those who admired and bought it (and those who collect now) find it difficult to categorize American Modern. Certainly it was not Art Deco - not geometric and no hard angular lies here. It was also in contradiction to the sleekness and coldness of much of the then current European design. Functional, it was not puristicly so. Called Surrealist by some, that term seems extreme, but its influence can be seen. Amazingly, it seemed to combine a small measure of the traditional primitive American and a large dosage of the abstract into functional items, each as an individual piece of amorphous ceramic sculpture. It created a totally new and different American look, that slipped easily into the everyday life around us. We were reassured that our instincts were right as it was featured in the leading museums (and remains so today), and it received the American Deisgner's Institute Award for the best ceramic design of 1941. Over 100 copies were made later by others. The style is still unique and best described by its designer - American Modern.

The glaze colors were as new as tomorrow. Subdued and greyed, almost muted, the original colors were Seafoam Blue, Granite Grey, Chartreuse Currey, Coral, Bean Brown and White. The designer had attempted to depart from the smooth primary colored "paint job" look of the dinnerware then on the market. He had turned instead to an underlying textural feeling in softly motled variegated self-tones in subtle earthy colors. Seafoam - a deep blue-green was a totally "new" color in pottery. Other aqua colors did not approximate it. Chartreuse Currey - sometimes referred to as "Seedless grape", was the color of the day. No other color was a fashionable as Chartreuse. Coral, soft and slightly speckled, blended easily in the new mix-n-match palette. The White was a soft warm white - not cold, not stark - but a lively eggshell. Granite Grey had a stone-like hue. Bean Brown, that ill-fated color, was almost a rusty red-speckled brown, but it had a short life and was discontinued during the war which followed. With peace came a replacement, and in 1950, Black Chutney, a black olive color, often foamy in glaze made its appearance. Cedar Green, a dark muted green, was also added. In 1955 Canteloupe (no other word describes it), and Glacier Blue appeared. Their comparative short production time accounts for their rarity. By January 1956, Seafoam, Chutney and Cedar Green were available only two times a year if the factory found it possible to produce them. All colors were popular in their own time and remain so today with collectors. Both White and Chartreuse were craze-prone and care had to be taken with them. Surprises remain for those who are collecting American Modern and are playing with these colors. Almost any mood can be achieved by pitting one color against its companions and a table setting to match any mood can be accomplished with the combination and substitution of colors. We have all shared the thrills of a "discovery" in the color combinations. Often Chartreuse, not generally the collector's favorite, is found to be a great mixing color. Russel Wright discovered these combinations after long evaluation and their complimentary values are not by chance.

Color was important in the success of American Modern, but shape contributed equally to its freshness. The coupe-shaped plate, a classic in design, was first introduced here. It was almost scoop shaped. The salad bowl was deep and round just right for tossing a salad. Its curved-in lid helped keep the vegetables in the bowl. The celery dish is an abstract leaf form. A new shape for a chop plate evolved - square with rounded corners which became convenient handles. The one-handled sugar bowl was a new idea as was the creamer - a miniature Aladdin's lamp. The relish rosette was a ceramic adaptation of an original spun aluminum piece of Wright design. The water pitcher is a classic of function and aesthetics. Considered as a single unit, every piece of American Modern survives as art embodied in dinnerware.

Today collectors are still finding a multiplicity of uses in individual pieces. The chop plate used as a tray, combines with teapot, creamer and sugar to form a tea set. The stoppered jug could be used for water, wine or hot liquids. Flowers or fruit make a perfect centerpiece using the salad bowl. The stack set pieces can be used as vegetable servers.

The basic quality of Steubenville Pottery was poor unfortunately, and that, more than any other factor, may account for the scarceness of it. It broke easily! "Small concern", the sales people said. It was "open stock", and you could replace it. Collecting it will take effort and expense for some items are very rare and all have become more costly as more and more people have sought it out. Rarities, experimental pieces and short production all influence availability today. In the early years of production, experimentation occurred and this practice continued, affecting supply during the twenty-year life span American Modern enjoyed. For production reasons, items which seem "standard" to our knowledge of the line today, were temporarily discontinued from time to time only to reappear later. Sales literature from various time periods list different items as available and this may account for scarcity of some items. Coffee pots, soups, the divided relish, relish rosette, the child's cup and saucer, and the carafe are examples. They went in and out of the line from time to time. In 1951 there were new additions - the stack set, the individual ramekin, coffee cup cover, divided vegetable, covered pitcher, hostess plate and mug were added. These should be found in all colors but Bean Brown, but they are difficult to locate and their late production accounts for their rarity. There is every reason to believe that the after-dinner coffee pot, sauce boat, and the childrens items, as well as the covered butter dish, were also later additions, coming some time between 1951 and 1959. The children's things and butter dish are rare and it is believed that not only were fewer of them made, but also, that the children's things were not made in all colors of that time period.

The production of American Modern which on the surface seems so uncomplicated, appears then to have been loosely structured and it is reasonable to assume that the pottery (whose production doubled with the success of American Modern) was forced to limit and change the line from time to time.

We can, however, put to rest one plaguing question and call it actually experimental. A bright Turquoise Blue color has been sighted from time to time, and knowing how often pottery workers dipped ware in colors of another line, we first assumed that was the case. With some frequency however, items of this color continued to appear and in time, the explanation just given did not satisfy. The recent finding of a divided vegetable (a late 1951 addition) in what collectors have named "Steubenville Blue" complicates our thinking until one considers that Seafoam, which is much like it, went into very limited production in 1956. It seems reasonable to assume that this new blue was an experimental attempt to return a comparable color to the line after Seafoam became unavailable. Cobalt used in nuclear research had doomed it. There is no evidence, however, that "Steubenville Blue" was ever more than an experimentation. Jobbers came to the pottery regularly buying seconds, experimental items, discontinued lines - any item which they could sell. Many "oddities" made their way out the back door of the pottery as did "Steubenville Blue".

The scarcity of salad plates today can be accounted for with the fact that they were not included in the starter sets. It follows that they were not always purchased so there were less made. Certainly there are some other items very difficult to find. Soups and fruits with their lugs are becoming scarce, as are pitchers, coffee and tea pots. Count the relish rosette, carafe, (inner lip rim or plain), ice box jar, coffee cup cover, covered individual ramekin, stack server, covered pitcher, butter dish and child's pieces as being rare. Still never seen is the myrtle wood stopper for the carafe, but you will find it pictured here. If this seems a loss, console yourself with the fact that in its last year of production (1959), Mr. Wright wanted to add zest to the serving pieces by putting wooden covers on the casserole, teapot and stack set! Too late in production, this was not done, but all those lidless serving pieces boggle a collector's mind. The missing divided relish is a mystery solved. This item had never been seen and could not be identified until a clue appeared in a newly-found press release from Russel Wright Accessories. It had a cane-wrapped handle! The "mint-tray", as we have been calling it, is the missing divided relish. Surely, it is the least functional of the serving pieces and that may account for its short life.

The ice box jar left all collectors guessing until we sorted it out from the individual ramekin. Both were the same size but one had a lid which covered the lip, the other nestled as in the sugar bowl. Every effort to ascribe the proper names to these two pieces ended in confusion and even associates of the designer were in disagreement on which was which. In fact, advertising suggests both uses for both items. We now know that the knobbed piece with nestled cover is the ice box jar. The covered individual ramekin covers the lip of the bowl which is actually the child's bowl. We should not be too surprised at this name confusion. Even the designer himself had several names for the same pieces - as in the carafe (jug), which was also called sherry pitcher, the stack set (nested serving bowls), the hostess set (lap plate), child's cup and saucer (after dinner cup and saucer), the individual ramekin could be stacked set, etc. It was as if once designed, a search for a just right name for the piece continued - and changed as new concepts evolved.

Most pieces of American Modern will be found with the mark indicated here, but a few smaller items were not signed. A familiarity with glaze colors will be your best guide in identifying children's pieces and mugs as well as cups and other items where the signature could not be used.

American Modern, in spite of its scarceness, is available in sufficient amounts to encourage one and a "set" is not an impossible dream. The challenges of rarities combined with the pleasures of owning and using the most popular and well-designed American dinnerware ever are compensating. Other designs and other lines followed - some more sophisticated and some more casual - but none were to make the mark of American Modern and none is more appreciated today. It is a classic without parallel in the pottery industry and the re-run of it's immense popularity is proof of the fact that good design transcends time.

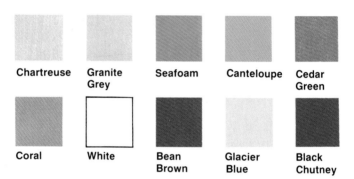

| Chartreuse | Granite Grey | Seafoam | Canteloupe | Cedar Green |
| Coral | White | Bean Brown | Glacier Blue | Black Chutney |

On Pricing American Modern

This first dinnerware line of Russel Wright remains the favorite among collectors and there is every indication that it will maintain and strengthen that lead. Rarities are indicated in the following list, but as stated in the preceding chapter, one should be aware that pitchers, lug soups and the coffee pots as well as the tea pots are becoming more difficult to find. Older collectors located these items with comparative ease and now, beginning collectors are having a harder time of it. Given a few years, the rarities list will be greater, therefore, than we find it today.

Some items stand out in this line as classic items, more tyical of the designer's work than others. Pitchers and celery dishes soon established themselves as favorite items with some collectors having mini-collections of water pitchers or celeries in all colors. All this would indicate that one has many ways to go with Russel Wright collecting and not everyone is set oriented. They *also* find a pattern to collecting American Modern. Many prices reflect rarity but you would do well to remember that while the butter dish carries a hefty position price wise, that price was somewhat artificially set early in the collecting days of American Modern and many dealers still hold to that price. True, it is rare, but other items such as the child's pieces, coffee cup covers, individual ramekin and covered refrigerator dish are much rarer and not as expensively priced.

The salad fork and spoon in American Modern colors were made by Steubenville as part of their Woodfield line - produced at the same time as American Modern. They are not Russel Wright items, but contractually he drew royalties from their sales because his glazes were used. Collectors now desire them as others did when sets were first made. They are nice companion pieces.

Color preferences remain as they were established early. Bean Brown and Black Chutney remain favorites as does the beautiful warm White. Expect to pay about 25% more for these colors. Canteloupe, Cedar Green and Glacier Blue, the later colors, enjoyed a smaller production time and are not easily found. These should also be considered as more expensive. Chartreuse, the favorite of many museums and the darling of its time, is not a favorite with collectors. For the present, think of Chartreuse as being at the low end of this price scale. Those who buy and sell American Modern should watch Chartreuse with care for it is the great mixing color of the palette, adding life and zest to most other colors. Given time and some experimentation by collectors, I feel Chartreuse will claim its deserved position as a popular color.

American Modern
Suggested Values

#300 Bread & Butter 6¼"	$2.50-3.50
#301 Salad Plate 8¼"	$4.50-5.00
#302 Dinner Plate	$5.50-6.00
#303 Cup	$7.00-7.50
#304 Saucer	$2.00-2.50
#305 Lug Soup	$8.00-10.00
#306 Chop Plate	$15.00-20.00
#307 Salad Bowl	$30.00-35.00
#308 Celery Dish 13"	$20.00-22.00
*#309 Divided Relish	$40.00-50.00
*#310 Relish Rosette	$40.00-50.00
*#311 Carafe (stoppered jug)	$35.00-50.00
#312 Covered Casserole 12"	$30.00-35.00
*#313 Ice Box Jar (refrigerator jar)	$40.00-50.00
#314 Covered Sugar	$8.00-10.00
#315 Creamer	$7.00-8.00
#316 Tea Pot 6" x 10"	$35.00-40.00
#317 Lug Fruit	$9.00-10.00
#318 Open Vegetable Bowl	$12.00-15.00
#319 Platter 13¾"	$12.00-15.00
#320 Water Pitcher	$35.00-40.00
#321 A.D.Cup & Saucer (Child's Cup and Saucer)	$15.00-20.00 set
#322 Coffee Pot 8" x 8½"	$35.00-40.00
#323 Salt	$5.00-6.00
#323 Pepper	$5.00-6.00
#324 Covered Vegetable 12"	$22.00-25.00
#325 Coaster Ash Tray	$10.00-12.00

#326 Gravy 10½"	$12.00-15.00
#327 Pickle Dish (liner for above)	$8.00-10.00
#328 Small Baker (vegetable dish) 10¾"	$12.00-15.00
*#329 Hostess Set w/Cup	$25.00-30.00
*#330 Coffee Cup Cover	$20.00-25.00
*#331 Covered Individual Ramekin	$40.00-50.00
#332 Divided Vegetable Dish	$25.00-30.00
*#333 Stack Server	$75.00-85.00
*#334 Mug (tumbler)	$20.00-25.00
*#335 Covered Pitcher 7½"	$50.00-55.00
#336 A.D. Coffee Pot 5" x 8"	$35.00-40.00
#337 Sauce Boat 8¼"	$10.00-15.00
*#338 Child's Plate	$17.00-20.00
*#339 Child's Tumbler	$20.00-25.00
*#340 Child's Bowl	$10.00-15.00
*#341 Covered Butter	$75.00-100.00
Salad Fork & Spoon	$35.00-40.00 pair

*Indicates scarcity or rarity

NOTE: Add 25% for White, Bean Brown and Black Chutney. Chartreuse should be at lower end of scale. Some items which in 1979 seemed commonplace to the collector are now difficult to find. Count all coffee pots, teapot and water pitcher among these.

American Modern Brochure, collector value $15.00.

Row I: Granite Grey mug, Canteloupe cup and saucer, Granite Grey stack set; Row II: Coral dinner plate, Seafoam salad plate, Granite Grey bread and butter, Granite Grey ice box jar, Coral individual ramekin; Row III: Coral gravy, Coral underplate (also called pickle dish), Glacier Blue covered casserole.

Row I: Cedar Green coffee pot, Black Chutney tea pot, Coral after-dinner coffee pot; Row II: Granite Grey salad bowl, Seafoam divided vegetable dish; Row III Coral sauce boat, Cedar Green small baker.

Row I: Granite Grey pitcher, Black Chutney soup, Seafoam fruit; Row II: White covered vegetable, Chartreuse covered pitcher; Row III: Coral carafe (stoppered jug), Glacier Blue shakers, Granite Gray divided relish.

Row I: Chartreuse open vegetable, Seafoam relish rosette; Row II: Bean Brow chop plate, Cedar Green coffee cup cover, White coaster ash tray, Woodfield fo and spoon in American Modern colors, Coral platter, Seafoam celery. Row I Chartreuse party plate and cup, Coral after-dinner cup and saucer, Coral child plate, Chartreuse child's tumbler, Glacier Blue child's bowl.

Iroquois Casual

The Iroquois chapter in this tabletop study is the mystery story of Russel Wright designs. In spite of the fact that Casual items are seen with some frequency, and advertisements for it are numerous, we still are left with questions unanswered in our search for real facts on the line. The Russel Wright papers at Syracuse University are not complete in this area and our information comes, for the most part, from advertisements of the years when it was sold, sales brochures, some limited correspondence in the files, and to a great extent from the actual finding of the articles and comparisons then made possible.

The evolution of the entire line is an obscure one to trace and the facts are not all "in" on its roots and its changes as time progressed. While there are those who may find our search for specifics pedantic, there are others engaged in serious study of styles and marks, searching for some chronological order. We must leave the Iroquois absolutes to their findings and, for this record, state what is known and/or believed to be the situation from the vantage of this date. Our records are clear that, in spite of constant restyling and redesigning, color changing and mark differences, from beginning to end, Iroquois Casual was always advertised as "new". "New", in this instance, is relative.

We must begin again however. The year was 1946 and flushed with the success of American Modern, the designer had no problem in finding a manufacturer for the new line on which he was working. The manufacturing problem now was to find a pottery which made fine quality dinnerware with the ability to produce a product which would not chip or break as easily as American Modern and which would go from refrigerator to oven to table with ease, which could be stacked and stored in a minimum of space. If it could be easily cared for, it was an advantage the designer established as important.

The Iroquois China Company, with its great expertise, was Russel Wright's choice and by this date, he could be the chooser. The contractural agreement was that Russel Wright would not design another dinnerware for a six month period after the Iroquois line was introduced and then not design a line within a 70% range to dealers. Royalties were established with a scale that included even seconds. As was customary in his standard contracts, he was to restyle or redesign pieces on the entire line if sales records showed the need for new or different pieces. A good portion of the confusion which collectors have with the Iroquois line stems from this multiplicity of pieces with little difference.

In no other of the Wright designs was the design clause used more frequently. In addition to major work in redesign and restyle, minor changes were many. We have now established six bowls, six cups and the same number of marks. Perhaps the sameness of these numbers is significant, but it all adds to confusion.

Wright's exclusive contract with Raymor had expired by this time and from that experience, he recognized that a large distributor with nationwide sales coverage was a requirement if his product was to continue to be a nationally used product. Since distributor commissions customarily amounted to the cost of manufacturing of the item itself, this choice of a good marketing agent was an important one. Garrison Products of New York City was chosen to distribute Iroquois and they were as active in merchandising it as Raymor had been with American Modern. It soon claimed American Modern's position as the best selling dinnerware and even in its late years, stores reported record sales. From beginning to end, Iroquois was merchandised expertly.

Purchasers were given Warranty Registration Certificates from the Mercantile Insurance Company dated and individually numbered, which guaranteed that the Iroquois china purchased would not break for one year from the date of puchase if given normal household usage and if purchased in service for four. One could have his item replaced free when the company received one-half of the broken item accompanied by a completed warranty form. A deluge of advertising followed and this was impressive advertising. Combined with the cook-and-serve capability, it put the homemaker on notice that there was a real departure in the dinnerware field. Much was made of the features which had become requirements in the planning stages and no feature was more exploited than that of its thermo-shock properties. Not only was the dinnerware oven-to-table, but one was told that with the use of an asbestos pad, a serving dish was safe on the stove top. Russel and Mary were pictured at dish breaking sessions trying to break a dish and emphasizing the advantage of the new product. Manufacturing details were made public information and it was real news that this was vitreous china fired at 2,300°. Its distribution was to jewelry stores and gift shops, as well as to large department stores, giving it more extensive sales coverage than American Modern. Garrison augmented the great job Raymor had started and the designer's name continued to dominate advertisements in national magazines.

Collectors today will find publicity details interesting regarding prices also. It was written that because of double usage, one need not own so many items. Given a backward look and knowing all the various items that were made, the fact seems to go begging. Something for everyone for every occasion seems more to the point.

The earliest of the Iroquois pieces were almost ⅜″ thick with an institution-like composition. It had rolling contoured lines with curved in finger grips on large pieces. A foamy mottled appearance caused by a crystallization in the glaze is characteristic. Thickness and the foamy look combined to give it an almost primitive appearance, and there are those who have felt these early pieces were of second quality. Not true. This textured look was the result of glaze work done at Alfred University in New York and was a desired effect. The original colors in 1946 were Sugar White, Lemon Yellow and Ice Blue, but Nutmeg, Avocado Yellow and Parsley Green followed almost at once. Lemon and Parsley were discontinued early, but appear again to round out the color chart.

In late 1951, new colors were still being added with a palette which by then included Charcoal, Ripe Apricot, Pink Sherbet, Lettuce Green, Oyster, Canteloupe, Aqua, Brick Red. Forest Green appears in the files but all evidence points to the fact that Forest was a late name given to the dark Parsley Green when it was re-introduced. The dates of Aqua and Brick Red are not known, but it seems probable that they were late colors produced only for a short time. The files also contain a reference to a Gray-blue and describe it as a cross between Ice Blue and Charcoal. I have seen nothing that fits that description, but I am still not willing to rule out the possibility that it was made.

Colors changed in intensity and gradation with frequency and not all items were made in all colors. There are two different shades of many of the colors and they were sold with little complaint from customers. The most probable cause is that suppliers of color oxides had changed or could have sent variant glaze oxides with a resultant color change. Formulas established would then have produced different colorations because of the materials furnished. Color variation was often expected and accounts were told in advance that a certain range percentage of color variation might result. Collectors will find these factors at work in Iroquois more than other Russel Wright lines and perhaps this is partly due to the long production time which no doubt involved more suppliers of materials.

Original designs are of the "pinch" look with surfaces rounded and curved, handles recessed and pinched in. There were no rims or grooves, fancy feet or handles. Handles, if not recessed, were thick, short and rounded. The elimination of rims from plates, cups and saucers reduced the diameter of these pieces for easy carrying on a tray. Flat covers meant even covered soups could be stacked and indented side handles took less space than the standard protruding ones. Even minute details like the foot of the saucer fitting tops of the cup were designed so the server could carry cups and saucers stacked.

Early restyling accomplished over a period of time influenced shapes only slightly - a light weight product was evolving, mottled glazes disappearing. The ware became more refined. A redesign came in 1951 and the newer colors were added at this time. However this does not rule out old colors or old items. All were sold interchangeably. The mix-n-match concept did not begin with the purchaser, as the manufacturer used a liberal amount of mixing of all colors and shapes, all as the sales need indicated. As late as 1952, the pinch look was still being advertised in new additions to the production, and by that date, the number of items had mushroomed to include the after-dinner coffee cup and saucer and the soup tureen.

In the redesigned ware, knobs were used to replace the old pinch look, handles were more loop-like and bowls seemed not so cushioned with a more Oriental look than with the old. The redesigned style sold side by side with the older ware. In some cases, the new handled covers were placed on the old bottoms and covers were sold separately. It seemed not to bother the designer or the manufacturer if the two styles were mixed. Collectors today, in sorting out these many items, have strong preferences for the original designed items or the redesigned items, however. Cups, bowls and covers of all sorts should be studied by those who would buy these items by mail. Bowls are especially confusing with the redesigned sugar bottoms doubling as a fruit bowl at one time. Bowl usage was interchangeable in fruits, soups, cereals, and serving pieces. Without lids the coffee pots were called pitchers. The salad bowl made a centerpiece or could hold the food of your choice. Whenever double usage could be contrived, it was mentioned as another item. All this in the real effort to lead the buyer to believe he was buying fewer pieces. At least one could rationalize that fact. The rule today would seem to be that one must not consider these lidless pieces as incomplete. They are of value for their second usage, and indeed, may have been bought that way. Coffee cups and saucers, as opposed to tea cups and saucers as well as the small platter, were early pieces which were dropped as the line evolved. These are exceptions however, as the tendency was to add.

The Iroquois story, detailed as it is, was to have another chapter. In the restyled shapes, patterned sets were offered in 1959. They were sold in 45-piece sets composed of 8 each of the dinner plates, bread and butter plates, cups, saucers and cereal bowls, a covered sugar and creamer, an open 8" vegetable bowl and the small platter. Very little of this patterned ware was made in comparison to the general production, but you may find it in several variations: Shepherds Purse - white beige and green flowers on the Ripe Apricot color, White Violets - violet veining in white blossoms, green leaves on Ice Blue, Orange Flower on a Lemon Yellow base, Woodhue on a Canteloupe base, Nasturtium - Orange Blossoms, three shades of green leaves on a Ripe Apricot ground, Gay Wings - Pink Blossoms, deeper pink veining on Pink Sherbet and more. The designs were executed by a copper plate engraving process applied under the glaze. All these naturalistic patterns are delicate and their treatment is tasteful, not detracting from the Oriental look of the redesigned ware, but actually complimenting it. Advertising on these patterns indicate that no two pieces in the same category had the same design, adding an interesting casual quality. These designs were not well received, and we find little of it available to us as collectors. It was short lived and has not become popular with collectors except as examples.

By this 1959 date, Iroquois had replaced its American Modern sister as the fastest selling dinnerware in the country. Clearly marked as *china*, not earthenware, Casual china by Russel Wright was a winner. It enjoyed this favored position for about twenty years; production cuts came in the mid-sixties. Although a large line from the beginning, twenty years of changes described add up to a tremendously large possible number of items and/or treatment of an item.

Those who find mark research interesting will find Iroquois marks a challenge. Even though used from the beginning in advertising, we find the word Casual was not used until later in marks. Early marks are those which say Russel Wright China by Iroquois. These words appear in two different colors at least and there are two different styles of the letter "I" in Iroquois. In addition, an unmarked cup and saucer in the earliest colors appears to have been an early example. Several marks including the word Casual were made. No one has been able to establish a chronological pattern to these marks as yet, for from the beginning to the redesign - piece to piece, color to color - there seems to be no common denominator. For now, with the facts as we have examined them, we have a reasonably accurate overview of items and dates. A more detailed study of marks must be left to those from whom we hope to hear later. Iroquois is a study with many students.

Cooking pieces to accompany and complement the dinnerware were available in the redesigned look. All have knobs typical of that style, all are signed and care instructions were clearly marked on each piece. They were made in later colors as well as white. All are elusive and all need tender care if you are to use them today. They are handsome additions to an Iroquois collection and may be among the more expensive items you will purchase.

Collecting Iroquois is rewarding as it is generally easier to find than are the other lines. This is probably due to the finer product made by Iroquois. More of it has survived. Given that fact, it still is a challenge, because of the many colors and the redesigning. Iroquois can result in a lovely delicate set or a sleek sophisticated set by experimentation with the mix and match colors. While one-color settings are attractive, discovering and achieving different effects with mixed color usage adds variety and multiplicity of uses - a Wright concept from the beginning. As with American Modern, new results in our trials with colors seem like discoveries to us, but I should assure you again that these effects were studied and achieved by the designer himself. When we find ourselves with a great new color combina-

by the designer himself. When we find ourselves with a great new color combination, we have followed Russel Wright's concept in his total plan for Iroquois dinnerware. Iroquois is a pleasure to collect and to use as growing numbers of collectors prove.

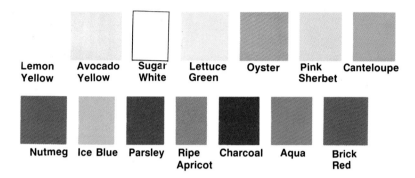

| Lemon Yellow | Avocado Yellow | Sugar White | Lettuce Green | Oyster | Pink Sherbet | Canteloupe |

| Nutmeg | Ice Blue | Parsley | Ripe Apricot | Charcoal | Aqua | Brick Red |

On Pricing Iroquois

As with American Modern, some Iroquois rarities exist and are indicated in the price list. In this large line, we also find scarcities are developing. Wine carafes, two years ago rather plentiful, seem to have disappeared into "sets" or wine carafe collections. So it goes with other items. Many early collectors assumed this large line would afford lots of opportunities to buy, and we have all been surprised that that is not always true. At the first sighting of after dinner cups that I am aware of, many would-be collectors turned away, waiting to find them in their choice of colors. Three years later, these turned out to be the only ones I've seen offered for sale. I'd consider them rare in any color. This seems to be the right place to mention the fact that you may come upon serving items by Iroquois not marked Iroquois by Russel Wright but in Russel Wright colors. These seem to be good companions, though not part of the line. Be aware of their existance as you see sets which may include flat rimmed serving pieces - Iroquois, but not Russel Wright even though his glazes were used and royalties were received on them. Color favorites have been reformed since my price guide *Russel Wright and His Dinnerware* was published in 1981. Sugar White and Charcoal, favorites then, have now become part of the general grouping and no longer enjoy favored positions. Brick Red and Aqua have assumed their position and these rare colors will be higher than the price scale by about one fourth. Canteloupe is a difficult and popular color. Look for it at the higher position. Ice Blue, now more popular than at first, has a respectable position as do all the other colors except Avocado Yellow, which must be thought of in terms of the low price. Do not overlook its lovely mixing qualities though.

In most cases, prices listed here apply alike to original designed, restyled and redesigned items. In some instances, prices are different and those are indicated. Lid prices are listed separately and should be thought of as an addition to the base price. Keep in mind the fact that all items are considered as wholes even without the lids.

Try to keep an open mind when finding your item on this Iroquois listing. If you have problems, try your judgement based on measurement combined with redesign features and the lid practice. You'll probably be right. If all else fails, write me. A picture of your item will help considerably and together we may add to this list of known items.

Russel Wright Casual China
By Iroquois
Suggested Values

Dinner plate 10"	$5.00-6.00
Luncheon plate 9½"	$4.50-5.00
Dessert & salad plate 7½"	$4.50-5.00
Bread & butter plate 6½"	$2.50-3.00
Tea cup & saucer 7 oz.	$8.00-10.00
*Coffee cup & saucer 9 oz.	$10.00-12.00
Redesigned tea cup & saucer 7 oz.	$8.00-10.00
Fruit bowl 9½ oz. 5½"	$4.00-5.00
Redesigned fruit 5¾"	$4.00-5.00
Cereal 5"	$5.00-6.00
Cereal - redesigned 5"	$5.00-6.00
Soup 11½ oz. 5¼"	$6.00-8.00
Redesigned soup 18 oz.	$6.00-8.00
*Covers for soup & cereal bowls 5¼" with steam opening	$6.00-8.00
Gravy bowl 12 oz. 5¼"	$6.00-8.00
Gravy stand 7½"	$3.00-4.00
Gravy cover (ladle slot) 6¾"	$5.00-6.00
Gravy with attached stand 16 oz.	$10.00-12.00
*Redesigned gravy - lid becomes stand	$20.00-25.00
Stacking sugar 4"	$8.00-10.00
Stacking creamer 7½"	$8.00-10.00
*Lg. family size stack creamer	$10.00-12.00
*Lg. family size stack sugar	$12.00-15.00
Redesigned sugar	$9.00-10.00
Redesigned creamer	$9.00-10.00
Butter dish - half pound	$45.00-50.00
*Restyled butter dish - quarter pound	$60.00-65.00
Stacking salt & peppers	$10.00-12.00 pr.
*Single salt	$20.00-25.00
*Pepper mill	$25.00-30.00

*Coffee pot body	$40.00-55.00
Coffee pot oval cover	$5.00-6.00
*Restyled tea pot (replaced coffee pot)	$50.00-55.00
*A.D. Coffee pot 4½"	$30.00-35.00
Cover for A.D. coffee pot	$5.00-6.00
Salad bowl 10" 52 oz.	$20.00-25.00
Water pitcher 5¼" 1½qt.	$15.00-20.00
Cover for above pitcher	$3.00-5.00
*Restyled water pitcher 2 qt.	$35.00-40.00
*Oval platter (individual) 10¼"	$20.00-25.00
Oval platter 12¾"	$12.00-15.00
Oval platter 14½"	$15.00-20.00
Open vegetable bowl $8^1/_8$" 36 oz.	$15.00-18.00
Open vegetable bowl or casserole 10"	$18.00-20.00
Open divided vegetable bowl or casserole 10"	$20.00-25.00
Cover for above	$6.00-8.00
Casserole 8" 2 qt.	$18.00-20.00
Casserole 8" 4 qt. same as tureen-deep	$30.00-35.00
Cover for above both items	$5.00-6.00
Chop plate $13^7/_8$"	$15.00-20.00
Mug 13 oz.	$20.00-25.00
*Restyled mug (tall coffee) 9 oz.	$25.00-27.00
Gumbo (flat soup) $8^3/_8$" 21 oz.	$12.00-15.00
*Wine or coffee carafe	$45.00-50.00
*Party plate with cup - as set	$20.00-25.00
*After-dinner coffee cup & saucer	$30.00-35.00
Cook-ware - all rare - all with restyled covers	
Dutch oven	$25.00-30.00
Covered fry pan	$25.00-30.00
Electric serving tray 17½" x 12¾"	$30.00-35.00
Percolator	$30.00-35.00
Covered sauce pan	$25.00-30.00
Hot plate	$20.00-25.00
3 qt. casserole	$25.00-30.00
4 qt. casserole	$27.00-35.00
6 qt. casserole	$30.00-35.00
Asbestos pad	$12.00-15.00
Basketry holders for all casseroles	$5.00-10.00

*Rare

**Coffee & tea pots become pitchers without lids.
Add 25% for Aqua and Brick Red. Avocado Yellow should be at low end
of scale.

Brick Red dinner plate; Ripe Apricot 1½ qt. covered pitcher; Nutmeg redesigned gravy with lid as stand; Oyster luncheon plate; Aqua salad plate; Charcoal bread & butter; Ripe Apricot 10″ divided covered casserole original lid;
White 10″ divided covered casserole redesigned lid; Avocado Yellow butter
dish; Aqua redesigned butter dish.

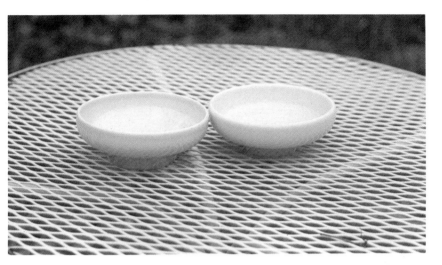

Sugar White restyled fruit bowl; Lemon Yellow restyled cereal.

ipe Apricot restyled water pitcher; Sugar White family-size creamer; Sugar White rge coffee pot; Note: Both creamer and coffee pot were made in smaller ver-ions - regular stack creamer and after-dinner coffee pot. Sizes pictured here are re.

Pink Sherbet hostess plate with cup; Lettuce Green 12¾″ platter; Charcoal original mug; Ice Blue redesigned mug; Charcoal redesigned tea pot; Nutmeg gumbo; Avocado Yellow stacking salt & pepper; Pink Sherbet 36 oz. open vegetable bowl.

Charcoal 1½ qt. water pitcher, no cover; Charcoal 4 qt. casserole, original style cover; Ice Blue after-dinner cup and saucer.

Charcoal covered soup; Ice Blue fruit dish; Pink Sherbet cereal bowl.

eft to right: Three early cup handles in what appears to be order of production. up #4 is the coffee cup, discontinued early and rare. Cup #5 is the later redesign- d handle. A sixth cup, thought to be the original cup, is pictured in the Potpourri ection.

Avocado Yellow 4½″ original tea pot; Nutmeg gravy, lid as stand; Oyster wine carafe; Oyster stacking cream & sugar; Aqua redesigned sugar; Ice Blue redesigned creamer; Lemon Yellow cup & saucer; Canteloupe 2 qt. covered redesigned casserole.

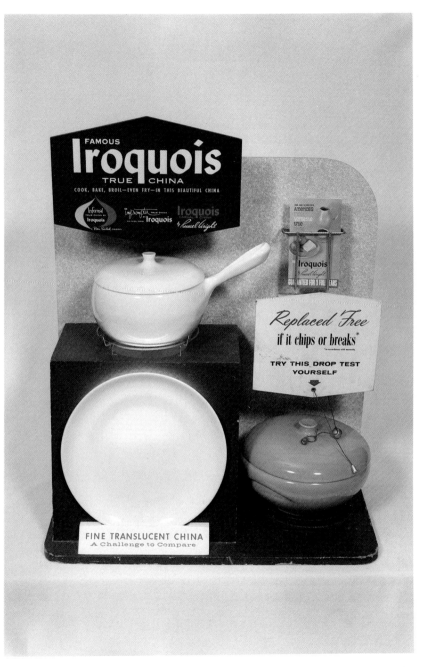

Iroquois store display sign from the pottery advertising collection belonging to B. A. Wellman.

Sterling Hotel and Restaurant Dinnerware

By 1948, Russel Wright's name and designs were well known and well accepted in the dinnerware field as well as the general home furnishing areas. Equally well established was the Sterling China Company, a leading producer of institutional dinnerware. It was inevitable that the designer wished to step into this area of tabletop designs and understandable that the leader in that industry would seek out his work.

Finding the glaze formulas to please the designer was one of the Sterling production problems. Doris Coutant, one of the most capable ceramists in the Wright firm, was sent to Wellsville, Ohio, to personally supervise the evolution of the glazes which had to be approved by both the company and the designer. Her job as well as her mission was difficult. The samples were tried repeatedly and the designer became impatient over the excessive attempts (he felt) to get them "right". His standards were the highest and what seemed like a simple color formula seemed to always fall short of his expectations when mixed and fired. Over and over samples were submitted, rejected and tried again. Finally the colors were approved as Ivy Green, Straw Yellow, Suede Grey, Cedar Brown, White, and Shell Pink. These were to be made as solid color institutional dinnerware. The Sterling Company was permitted to adapt these solid colors to their own use, decorating them with customers' logos, signatures, emblems or appropriate theme designs. Be aware that the *designs* were not Russel Wright designs, but were put on his shapes. In spite of this, some handsome services evolved and some are much sought after.

As in the other lines discussed, the designer drew royalties when his glazes or shapes were used, regardless of design. My best advice is that if one's eye catches a design that pleases, he had best get all of it he can at once for very likely he will never find that same design again. Custom designs were many, but none was extensive.

If the designer was certain of his color requirements, Sterling, with its own field of expertise, had definite requirements for the pieces which were to be made. They knew in advance what items a hotel or restaurant needed, and they knew serving size. They also knew that their market was established pricewise and that this dinnerware must conform to the established price scales. The designer, who liked departure from the usual, felt constrained but the buyer won out. An amusing bit of information illustrates this. Mr. Wright felt a 10 oz. tea pot was too small, but the President of the Sterling Company wrote him that he felt he'd not considered that an extra amount of water would weaken the tea badly. Additionally, he wrote, "This is the size that sells. All are made, but 10 oz. is the volume item in the tea pot line." They liked Wright's 10 oz. coffee bottle, feeling it provided a smart appearance and was good because in "nice places" one expects two cups of coffee.

The Russel Wright line was Sterling's trial at testing the homemarket as well as the commercial market and it is to the credit of both parties that they set aside pre-made judgments and worked to achieve such a practical design which worked well in the home as well as the institution. A design that was new in its own field and items with soft cushioned lines and ease of serving resulted. With

Iroquois-like handles and lines, it fulfilled its potential and met the needs of both markets. It remained in production until 1950.

The Sterling Company advertised this new line to the restaurant trade, and as the designer had done before with American Modern and Iroquois, they emphasized ease of service and multiple usage.

Five sizes of plates were made: 11½" service plates, 10¼" dinners, 9" luncheons, 7½" salads and 6¼" bread and butters. With a slow upward curve of the edges from the center, a rolled edge which hid the foot resulted. Serving without touching the food or little of the eating surface resulted.

The tea cup held 7 oz. and had a jiggered-on handle which made it seem to be actually a part of the cup. It was an average serving, but the cup appears larger than ordinary. The saucer was deep, protecting table linen from spillage.

The demi-cup also appears to have an unusually generous capacity but it held the usual 3½ oz. The handle is unusual as it curves downward not touching the body of the cup.

Finger-grip depressions reduced breakage on the sugar cover. With no handle, the sugar bowl itself seemed more practical.

The 9 oz. cream pitcher with a handle like the cup, had a lip especially designed to cut down on dripping.

The individual creamers with 1 oz. for coffee or tea and 3 oz. for cereal or dessert are tiny graceful gems.

The fruit bowl had multiple uses - dessert or ice cream. Its use was limited only by the cook's imagination.

The bouillon had two lugs extending outward and slightly downward. Molded to the shape, they withstood breakage.

The four compartment relish was especially nice for restaurant usage where menu dividends were offered. It was used for relishes, jams, jellies and the like. High partitions prevented foods from running together and were deep enough to prevent spoons from falling out. In the home, it was a useful buffet piece.

Four sizes of platters were available, their uses unlimited, their shapes rolled like the plates.

The coffee bottle served double duty for coffee or hot water for tea. It also had an integrally molded handle. One had to remove the cover to pour but it had a two finger grip rather than a knob. It took less room than a coffee pot, yet held two cups. Both the designer and manufacturer were *very* proud of this item and collectors have taken it to their hearts also.

The 10 oz. tea pot also had a finger grip depression but the cover remained in place while pouring. The absence of inside rims simplified draining and drying. Watch this item. It is so small that collectors can confuse it with a creamer if it is found without the cover.

The sauce boat also can be a confusing item. It held 5 oz. only and had the same open curved half handle as the demi cup. It was useful for sauces or syrups, but is NOT another cream pitcher.

The soup bowl appeared to be an overly generous size also but held 14 oz. It could be used for grapefruit set in ice or for sauce desserts. Being deep, it retained heat from soups.

The 23 oz. salad bowl was intended for individual salads served as a main course. It was an ideal fruit bowl also.

The celery tray, 11 inches long, had the cushioned edge rim but the end edges sloped down slightly to form handles - much the same feeling as the American Modern butter dish.

The ash tray is the classic piece of this line, and according to some, one of the very best pieces of all Russel Wright designs. It is gently curved with a matchbook compartment. It is ideally sized - a masterpiece of design.

The water pitcher, as originally designed, was a departure from the spherical shape. With a two quart-capacity, it had a molded handle. This item was redesigned and a modified tilted jug style more graceful and less chunky resulted.

A 10 oz. onion soup was covered with the grip cover and was just right for an individual casserole.

This completes the Sterling line descriptions as we know it now, but it will leave some readers asking, "What about the vase you mentioned in your *Russel Wright and His Dinnerware* Price Guide? There is another chapter in the Sterling Story. Read on.

Some maverick pieces of Russel Wright Sterling, quite unlike the ones we have been discussing, have surfaced. They have an oriental feeling and are characterized by white ruffled edges on a glossy black base. We know pieces were designed by others on the Wright staff but accepted by him and these are an example of that practice. Drawings exist of a chop plate, soup and underplate and the vase has turned out to be a Sake bottle with stopper. Those who have seen it have conjectured that these may have been designed for the Shun Lee Restaurant in New York City, and the shape name of Polynesian would indicate that possibility. That guess took us again to the Sterling files at Syracuse University where we find line drawings of the ware dated 1965. The drawings list Sterling itself as the client. Shun Lee, a New York restaurant, was to have been a total involvement project from "first to last." In the Shun Lee files we find no mention of any dinnerware but the time frame is the same - 1965. Some of Wright's associates tell me that Shun Lee never really "bought" the total concept presented to them, and feel that they never used unusual dinnerware, much less anything designed by Russel Wright. The results are still out with some believing the dates too coincidental and that it must be Shun Lee dinnerware, but others offering no better answer cannot accept that possibility. My inclination is to agree that this is a proposed line for Shun Lee. It may have been only prototyped by Sterling, but some does exist. By the date of this design, however, Wright was no longer working regularly with the Sterling company, and it seems likely that in planning the total concept in 1965, he would turn to the institutional pottery he had worked with before. The absence of mention of it in the Shun Lee files could indicate that it was part of the concept they did not agree to, and this would explain its rarity. Whatever its obscure roots, this appropriately named Polynesian line has a legitimate place in our look at the sterling production with facts and conjecture as they now appear.

Collectors agree that Sterling is difficult to find, but if one spots some it is likely to be bonanza time for where a bit is found there is very likely to be more. This results from its being located primarily as "old stock" in restaurant supply houses. There have been several instances where buyers were able to find many pieces in such places with the owners glad to be rid of obsolete stock. Try it - you may hit a bonanza yourself.

Ivy Green	Shell Pink	Suede Grey	Straw Yellow	Cedar Brown

On Pricing Sterling

Given the fact that there is less Sterling than most of the other Russel Wright dinnerware, it should not be surprising that there are also fewer collectors. Those who seek it out, however, are as relentless in their search and as enthusiastic in their collecting as are any others. In many cases, I have heard from collectors of one of the other lines who collects Sterling as an every-day usage line because of its extreme practicality and the diversity of its usage. Having noticed no real trend toward color preference, I do find the plain ware is preferred to the patterned items. As mentioned, the ash tray is one of the classic designs in all of Wright's work and many collectors seek it out whether they are Sterling collectors or not. The coffee bottle is a favorite also. With both these items, there are those collectors who confine their collecting to "one of each color" as we have seen with other items. That is very likely the reason we are finding prices on these to have escalated. In general, it may seem that this institutional ware is being priced out of proportion to the finer quality dinnerware lines. That it brings these prices is due largely to the fact that there is simply not much of it around and collectors who seek it out often must over-pay by buying out a supply house. They may then be forced to sell their extra items at a higher price because of having had such a large original outlay of funds. Whatever the cause, Sterling is a great line and deserves our respect on its own merits. Our listing may be considered complete with the exception of possible future findings in the Polynesian-shaped ware. Prices on Polynesian are not established, but pieces are very rare.

Sterling
Suggested Values

Service plate 11½″	$6.00-8.00
Dinner plate 10¼″	$5.00-6.00
Luncheon plate 9″	$4.00-5.00
Salad plate 7½″	$3.00-4.00
Bread & butter plate 6¼″	$2.00-3.00
Cup 7 oz.	$5.00-7.00
Saucer 6¼″	$2.00-3.00
*Demi cup 3½ oz.	$10.00-12.00
*Demi saucer	$3.00-5.00
Fruit 5″	$4.00-6.00

Bouillon 7 oz.	$7.00-8.00
Oval platter 7$^1/_8$"	$6.00-8.00
Oval platter 10½"	$8.00-10.00
Oval platter 11¾"	$10.00-12.00
Oval platter 13$^5/_8$"	$12.00-13.00
Celery 11¼"	$9.00-11.00
Divided relish 16½"	$14.00-16.00
*Individual cream 1 oz.	$4.00-6.00
*Individual cram 3 oz.	$6.00-8.00
Cream pitcher 9 oz.	$6.00-8.00
Covered sugar 10 oz.	$8.00-10.00
Sauce boat 9 oz.	$12.00-16.00
Onion soup 10 oz.	$12.00-15.00
Soup bowl 6½"	$8.00-10.00
Salad bowl 7½"	$8.00-10.00
Water pitcher 2 qt.	$25.00-27.00
Restyled water pitcher	$27.00-30.00
Tea pot 10 oz.	$25.00-27.00
*Coffee bottle	$30.00-35.00
*Ash tray	$40.00-50.00

Russel Wright with Sterling dinnerware and American Modern goblets. Circa 1948.

Cedar Brown 3 oz. creamer; Ivy Green redesigned pitcher; Cedar Brown 1 oz. creamer; Cedar Brown 11½″ service plate; Suede Grey A.D. cup and saucer; Ivy Green 10¼″ dinner plate; Straw Yellow 9″ luncheon plate; Ivy Green 7½″ salad plate; Cedar Brown 6¼″ bread & butter; Cedar Brown cup & saucer; Straw Yellow divided relish.

Cedar Brown tea pot; Cedar Brown original pitcher; Suede Grey ash tray; Ivy Green 13 $\frac{5}{8}$″ platter; Cedar Brown 11¾″ platter; Ivy Green soup; Ivy Green 7$\frac{1}{8}$″ platter; Cedar Brown bullion; Straw Yellow cream pitcher; Cedar Brown sugar bowl; Straw Yellow fruit.

hell Pink custom design plates; Polynesian-shape chop plate; Custom white
reamer; Polynesian tray; Polynesian sake bottle w/no stopper; Polynesian din-
er plate.

Highlight - Paden City Pottery Co. - Justin Tharaud

The contract between Russel Wright, the designer, Justin Tharaud, the marketing specialist, and the Paden City Pottery Company and Paden City Glass Company was signed in 1948 and design work began at that early date. The new design was to be called Highlight and its companion glassware was named Snow Glass. Collectors today use all the above names to indicate this same line.

Troubled from the start, it seems a testament to the confidence of all concerned that it ever made production. The designer contacted Justin Tharaud to be the distributor. His name was synonomous with high style and he seemed the logical choice to function at the business end of Highlight's marketing. Tharaud agreed to distribute the line with some restrictive principles of his own. Wright was to agree that Justin Tharaud had the exclusive rights to Highlight. The product was to be sold more reasonably than American Modern or the Iroquois line and the designer must agree not to design another dinnerware as long as his royalties averaged $10,000 a year, beginning with three years from the start of production. Additionally, he was to agree to the production of white, other colors or patterns if the new glaze colors were not readily accepted by the public. Tharaud received these assurances from Wright and in return, received the benfits of the designer's standard contract with the usual redesign clause, and altered only to accomodate the provisions as stated. Wright had wanted a flat fee of $15,000 on submission of designs whether they were approved or not and not contingent on successful manufacturing or sales. This was the first of the many differences that typified Highlight's life span. Justin Tharaud, predictably refused this clause.

After protracted negotiations all seemed settled, production began, and advertising was launched. With that Wright and Tharaud, both respected leaders in their areas of expertise, started a conflict of egos which never ended and every minor problem brought a torrent of accusations, blame, and general expressions of dissatisfaction. Almost comic are the letters Tharaud received referring him to an advertisement in which Wright's name was not the largest print on the page.

Tharaud would be called to task for this repeatedly and he would respond that he also was well established in the home furnishing field, that his own name had customer attraction and another well-spring would be opened with "You contacted me, I didn't seek you out." Like a family quarrel, a whole host of wrongs were brought up.

The line was soon to be in trouble. Costs were more than had been anticipated and it quickly became competitive with American Modern and Iroquois. In an effort to remedy that, the price was cut, leaving the margin of profit as well as royalties smaller. Neither man was pleased with that situation and each held the other responsible, directly or indirectly. Quietly the third party involved, The Paden City Pottery, basked in the pleasure of seeing Highlight capture the same sort of awards Steubenville and Iroquois had won. Highlight won the 1951 Museum of Modern Art Home Furnishing exhibit which toured this country and Europe. The Merchandise Mart in Chicago and the Museum of Modern Art co-sponsored it in their Good Design 1951 exhibit and it won the Trail Blazer Award given by the Home Furnishings League. Our sources do not indicate that the manufacturer was ever a party to the constant conflict that surrounded the dinnerware. When all was said and done, both parties did live up to their contractural agreements and the Pottery had little cause for complaint.

By 1953 the Paden City Glass Company had ended its production and the search for a producer of Snow Glass was fruitless. Both men felt the other should have been more aggressive in involving another glass company. Wright himself had exhausted many possible sources. He felt he had by this time worked for five years with little return. Tharaud was equally unhappy and with no alternative, the designer replaced snow Glass with like pottery pieces. Additions and redesigns were also done at this time. With no real help, sales continued to suffer and production soon ended. One must wonder what the future of Highlight might have been had it not been the arena for such bitter struggles. Surely this line would have fared better if it had not been used as a weapon in a dual of two strong personalities. Its fate, however, seemed sealed in the high cost of its manufacturing. That it could have held on much longer is doubtful for its life span ended at a time when the great potteries themselves were closing in the 1950's.

The name Highlight comes from the appearance of the white clay which shows through at rims and edges of the pieces, giving a highlighted effect. The colors which were made set it apart as a bit different. Reflecting the designer's own favorites, earth-tones or dark shades, the dinnerware was offered in Blueberry, Nutmeg, Pepper, Citron, White and a dark Green. The green and white are late additions (1951), and there was less made than the other colors. White was given the name Snow Glaze, and it replaced the Snow Glass. At the time of original production, Highlight had a soft matte glaze. A high gloss process was a later attempt to boost sales. Sleekly contoured lines with moulded handles, exaggerated lips and cushioned edges, Highlight can be called the most sophisticated of the Wright dinnerware. Where it was possible in other lines to say with correctivity there was "something for everyone", this is untrue with Highlight. It is a refined design, a cool, sleek controlled, tastefully executed design aimed at those who were a notch above the rest of us in our appreciation of art in dinnerware. Not trendy, it was an elegant statement, which used some of the Sterling lines with no compromise in high style.

Innovative as it was, the Snow Glass companion concept pushed it even further ahead of other dinnerware designs. Snow Glass, as Highlight, was a descriptive name. The body of the glass appears crystaline with tiny flecks of milk glass resembling snow particles suspended in it at randomly close intervals. It is textured in feel as well as appearance - a totally new and different concept. Be assured that you will probably not mistake it in a glass crowd. Almost translucent, it is distinctive. A probable European look-alike is easily distinguished as different as it has a lesser density of flakes and ground bottoms. Snow glass is of lesser quality and more milky. A familiarity with the list of items in which it was made will eliminate glass which is imitative. At the inception, the glass pieces were not only the three sized tumblers, but were also the salad plates, saucers, fruit dishes, various lids and at least a pitcher, a round bowl and an oval bowl cover which could double as a platter. Sugar lids also became small trays. These pieces were made in pottery after the glass was discontinued. At the same time (1953), the salt and peppers, butter dish, soups and pitcher were redesigned and the possibility exists that there may be more than one version of some of these items. All Paden City things are difficult to find, and this can be attributed, no doubt, to a short production of certain items within that short time frame. Collectors today feel fortunate to find examples in any color and the whole line is a challenge to them. It is most often found in groupings of one color rather than what would have been mixed or matched sets. Snow Glass remains very elusive and one suspects that it may have become separated from its pottery companion and may be lost in the larger area of glass collecting. There is every reason to believe, however, that the items on our list were actually produced. The files at Syracuse University show drawings, accepted drawings and actual advertising, attesting to the existence of all the items. Still, actual sightings on some things are few, and we must consider the entire line as the rare one in Russel Wright dinnerware. There are also many who consider it his best effort - a culmination of the best designs achieved with experience gained in the other successful patterns.

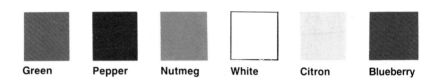

| Green | Pepper | Nutmeg | White | Citron | Blueberry |

On Pricing Highlights

Generally speaking, one color is as sought after as the other in Highlights and even Citron, which is a cousin to Steubenville Chartreuse and Iroquois Avocado Yellow, has a respectable place in the Paden City Line. We can find no reason for price variation based on color. Snow Glass items are all rare and comparatively very expensive when found. The pottery items which replaced Snow Glass seem high but collectors know that there were fewer of these pieces made and they are priced accordingly. I would not discourage you in your search for Paden City, for I believe it is possible to put together a set of this ware - but I believe you must be the sort who enjoys the hunt, who can wait for the "right thing" to come along and who will expect to pay more to acquire it. Most collectors of Highlights consider it their "good" set and add to it as frequently as possible, but who also collect and use another line in addition. If there is an "advanced collector" Russel Wright line, this is it.

Highlights
Suggested Values

Pottery items - Original Listing and 1953 additions believed to be complete.

Dinner plates	$10.00-15.00
Bread & butter plates	$4.00-6.00
Cups	$10.00-15.00
Sugar bowl	$10.00-15.00
Creamer	$12.00-15.00
Salt & pepper (2 sizes)	$15.00-20.00
Soup/cereal bowls (2 sizes)	$10.00-15.00
Cover for onion soup	$10.00
Covered pitcher	$45.00-50.00
Relish server	$30.00-35.00
After dinner cups & saucers 5 oz.	$35.00-40.00 set
Tea pot	$50.00-60.00
Butter dish	$75.00-80.00
Small platter (round)	$20.00-25.00
Small platter (oval)	$20.00-25.00
Large platter (oval)	$20.00-25.00
Gravy boat	$25.00-30.00
Mug	$30.00-35.00
Round salad or vegetable dish	$20.00-25.00
Divided vegetable	$30.00-35.00
Oval vegetable bowl	$20.00-25.00
Casserole (Bain Marie)	$45.00-50.00

Late (1953) pottery additions

Salad plates	$6.00-8.00
Saucers	$3.00-5.00
Cover for sugar bowl	$5.00-8.00
Vegetable bowl covers	$10.00-12.00
Sherbet or fruit dishes	$8.00-10.00

Snow Glass items

Salad plates	$15.00-20.00
Saucers	$10.00-12.00
Sugar cover (tray)	$15.00-18.00
Ice tea tumbler 14 oz.	$30.00-35.00
Water tumbler 10 oz.	$20.00-25.00
Juice tumbler 5 oz.	$20.00-25.00
2 pt. pitcher	$45.00-50.00
Oval vegetable cover (or platter)	$30.00-35.00
Round salad or vegetable bowl	$40.00-50.00
Sherbet/fruit dishes	$20.00-25.00
Shakers	$25.00-30.00 pr.
Candlesticks	$50.00-75.00 set

Pepper platter; Citron round vegetable bowl; Citron dinnerplate; Pepper sugar with Snow Glass top; Snow Glass salad plate; Blueberry bread & butter; Pepper shakers; Blueberry covered oval vegetable; Citron covered sugar; Pepper creamer; Pepper oval vegetable bowl; Snow Glass round vegetable bowl.

Citron sugar lid or tray; Blueberry oval vegetable bowl; Blueberry platter; Pepper fruit; Snow Glass Tumbler; Snow Glass sugar lid or tray; Snow Glass saucer; Pepper redesigned soup/cereal; Blueberry soup/cereal.

The Harker Story

Other writers have looked to Russel Wright's work for the Harker Pottery and find the first evidence of compromise in his work. The end, they feel, was omened by his patterned White Clover line. Certainly no one can argue that this new dinnerware was a departure from his earlier designs, but this writer is inclined to be more charitable in looking for the reasons why he turned to pattern after such successful solid colored achievements. I'll differ not in results, but in reason.

In 1951 all things combined to add to Russel Wright's credentials. American Modern and Iroquois were outselling all other dinnerware in retail stores. Sterling ware was popular and Highlights was an award winner. His various other products were doing well, many of them had been awarded prestigious awards and his name had become a household word, inescapable if one read newspapers or magazines. This does not add up, I feel, to a person in his declining years of work, willing to compromise his artistic values or his philosophy. Rather, I feel it does describe a man who was more self assured, who could break with his former style and with confidence look for the best in another concept. True, he had from the first espoused the values of solid colored wares, but Wright had matured a bit and was living very close to nature in the little house on the road at Garrison. By choice his leisure had come to include an appreciation of nature and although not a trained naturalist, he did find such a secure position in the woods that he was never very far from it for the rest of his days. What is certain, he was beginning a lifelong love affair with the earth and all that grew there, and his work reflected this preoccupation. He had always put "self" into his work and it seemed right to continue. Career-wise, it may have been an unfortunate choice, but the designer was confident enough to put his emotions in his designs and had no reason to expect less than approval. Approval from his peers was quick. The Museum of Modern Art not only acquired a set, it awarded the line their Good Design Award.

His daughter Ann, shares the story that the sketches for White Clover were done on long train rides home to the north from Florida. His work was never far from his hand and his eye was turning more frequently to the land.

It is sad then to know that White Clover did not do well on the market. The fault seemed not to be in its silk screen engraved-like decoration, but rather in the fact that it was in direct competition with American Modern and Iroquois Casual as Highlight had been. These were formidable competitors and with a higher price; White Clover came out the loser. In 1955 shortly before the end of its production, prices on it were reduced and with this lesser profit margin, Harker did not want to continue the line. All the old old advertising procedures had failed. If White Clover were oven proof, chip proof, detergent resistant and craze proof, so was Iroquois Casual, and it was cheaper. National advertising had been broad with ads in most home furnishing magazines. However, the ads appear to be fewer, possibly because of its short life but maybe attributable to the fact that for the first time, no distributor was involved in this dinnerware line. Harker and the designer had "gone it alone" and this may have had a telling effect. Wright extended himself in every way over this unfortunate line. He was not accustomed to failures and he labored to avoid that result with Harker - to no avail. Harker closed out the entire line as soon as possible after the price reductions were made.

All of this, of course, adds up to a reduced production and a dinnerware seen less often by collectors today. It does not make it less desirable or less sought after, but collectors now are fewer, as buyers were in 1955.

Look for White Clover in Meadow Green, Golden Spice, Coral Sand and Charcoal. Green had been presented at trade shows first, but the other colors followed almost at once. All continued for the life of the ware. This engraved clover design (some four leaf clovers are sprinkled in) is a classic in decorated ware as it differs totally from the standard ornamentation of the time. You will not confuse it with his other works, but you may find the marks non-existant or difficult to see, almost filled-in with glaze on the white underside of items. Some color-glazed bottoms have been found unsigned. Not every piece was clover decorated, but were intended to be used plain, adding interest to a table setting. In some instances, an item meant to be patterned is found plain. Potters at play, no doubt. You will notice only slight color variations in White Clover and we may expect that this uniformity resulted from its being made in such a relatively short time. The casserole was called a Shrimp and Egg Casserole in the advertising, and if you bought it you got the recipe. Would-be gourmets fortunately must have found other uses for it. The pitcher has an inner-locking lid which holds it securely when pouring. The shakers were sold as pairs with the tall one for salt and the short one for pepper. Sets are often found with a pair of the same size, and we can expect that stores allowed choices in them. From the first the sugar bowl was considered to be an individual ramekin and sold as such. Had White Clover been produced longer, we can be certain there would have been many more items with more specific uses.

As the other potteries had done, Harker made items out of their other lines and used White Clover colors. I am aware of cake lifters and pieces designed with metal to become servers of several sorts. A possible salad set also appears to combine the open vegetable bowl with a small Harker bowl. None of these were Russel Wright designs but they are all nice companion pieces. As was customary, royalties were paid to him on these items because of the use of his glazes. The General Electric clock made in 1953 used the Harker colors and the signature.

This was a short but well executed line in the Russel Wright family of dinnerware lines. Do not sell it short yourself for it is worth seeking. The luck of the clover will be with you if it comes to you easily. It is all considered to be difficult to find.

Golden   **Meadow**   **Coral**   **Charcoal**
Spice   **Green**   **Sand**

On Pricing White Clover

I find no real difference derived from color in the value of White Clover items. All are equally desired. It is early in its popularity with collectors and so there is not certainty about rarities. We can however consider its history and conclude that it all is elusive. Solid colored items are just as valuable as clover decorated ones since a set is incomplete without their addition. Do not pass them by if you would collect it. As with the other lines, remember that salad size plates were not included in the 16-piece starter sets and fewer were made of those then other size plates. The companion items are not plentiful and are worth consideration; but none should be of more value than other Harker ware.

Harker Ware
Suggested Values

Tea cup - clover decorated	$6.00-8.00
Tea saucer - color only	$2.00-3.00
6" Bread & butter plate - color only	$3.00-4.00
7⁵/₈" Salad plate - color only	$5.00-6.00
9¼" Dinner plate - clover decorated	$5.00-7.00
10" Jumbo plate - clover decorated	$6.00-7.00
11" Barbeque plate - color only	$10.00-12.00
Fruit dish - clover decorated	$3.00-5.00
Cereal/soup - clover decorated	$6.00-8.00
Gravy boat - clover decorated	$12.00-15.00
8¼" Covered vegetable dish	$20.00-25.00
8¼" Open vegetable dish	$15.00-20.00
7½" Open vegetable dish	$10.00-12.00
11" Chop plate - clover decorated	$15.00-20.00
2 qt. Covered casserole - clover decorated	$25.00-30.00
Covered sugar (individual ramekin)	$10.00-12.00
Creamer - clover decorated	$7.00-8.00
2 qt. Covered pitcher - clover decorated	$25.00-30.00
Salt & pepper - either size as set	$15.00-20.00
13¼" Platter - clover decorated	$15.00-20.00
Divided vegetable dish - clover decorated	$20.00-25.00
Ash tray - clover decorated	$8.00-10.00
General Electric clock	$50.00-60.00

Store display showing Harker White Clover is contrast with other decorated designs of 1951. Stainless steel and glasses not Russel Wright designs.

Meadow Green: Divided vegetable; Covered water pitcher; Vegetable dish 8¼"; Fruit; Cereal/soup.

Coral Sand 10″ jumbo plate; Golden Spice 11″ barbecue plate; Coral Sand
sugar and creamer; Coral Sand 13¼″ platter; General Electric Charcoal clock;
Meadow Green salt, Golden Spice pepper; Coral Sand fruit and soup/cereal;
Coral Sand 7⅝″ salad plate; Charcoal bread & butter plate; Golden Spice
plate adapted to tid-bit server; Coral Sand cup and saucer; Golden Spice 8¼″
open vegetable.

Knowles Esquire Line

In spite of White Clover's poor sales record, Russel Wright immediately replaced its void with his Knowles line in 1955. Some feel it reflected his disillusionment and lack of direction. I choose to feel it showed a measure of his sense of worth as a designer, evidenced by the fact that he would design a line so obviously Orientally inspired at a time when "Made in Japan" was an anethema in the pottery industry. Pottery giants were closing their plants because of the flood of Japanese imports, by no means restricted to their typical national design. Clearly, the designer had specific reasons for such a departure in American dinnerware and dared to risk censure by the industry. With grumblings, American pottery made room for Russel Wright's lines done on the Esquire shape - but for a limited market and not for long. It was designed at the height of his career and was another attempt to be different - by re-introducing pattern in a new treatment.

The Esquire shape, obviously eastern influenced, was decorated with naturalistic designs carrying out the oriental theme. Wright achieved something very different from anything then being made, reflecting his interest in nature and also his involvement with Asia where he was visiting often and would continue to work. He had found new inspiration and admired the cleanness of the Japanese line, their efficiency, their economy, their restraint. From this period on, we are able to see the great influence of the Japanese and the eastern design he had always admired.

The plans for Esquire were to market it in lower-priced stores that did mail order, such as Sears and Montgomery Ward. It was intended to be used as a premium with stamp concerns such as S and H and used as sales incentives by other companies. The Jewel Tea Company was approached as were grocery store chains. As his institutional line had been with Sterling, this new line was specifically directed to a different buyer. This was not designed for *House and Gardens* or *Better Homes and Gardens* readers, but for those who saved stamps for premiums or whose shopping took them to catalogues from less expensive establishments. Lest you think of this as a second-class line, I should say here that much care went into its planning. Scores of designs, all suitably executed to compliment the delicate shape, were tried and rejected. Even when the sketches were approved, the factory's attention was called to the fact that there existed the possibility that if the shape was not to be used exclusively for the Wright designs, buyers might confuse other's work with Wright's. In no uncertain terms, Knowles was told he must approve all sales literature in advance to avoid that circumstance.

The seeds of its failure were in the pottery itself. It simply did not photograph well, leaving such faint decorations unclear and the firms who would have marketed it soon found that flaw. Sears and Montgomery Ward would not buy at any price. They had been very interested at the prospect of using his designs but their catalogues could not picture it. The effort was made to add gloss to the glaze but uniformity was difficult to achieve and it was difficult to see such a change in photographs. Sales problems from all accounts developed quickly and by 1958, he learned that the S & H Stamp Company had had to take a loss on almost 1000 sets. Mail order retailers would not re-order. Salesmen who had had many orders at the trade shows found their dealers had put it in dead storage. Surveys were quickly sent out and complaints ranged from the poor photography standards to complaints that knife marks on the glaze were too numerous and sales people had no confidence in the line. Wright dismissed complaints with the statement that the sales people's refusal to promote it was at fault. Whatever the reason or combination of reasons, Knowles reported that they were "completely stuck with 3000 sheet editions of these decals." They proposed to run a very low priced sale to "move it" and would "probably let the line run its course and move on to other shapes and decoration." The glazes had already been changed, as noted, and the designer offered to drop all decorations and execute new ones. "The customer must be made to forget the old lines" he suggested. He offered to design additional pieces, even offered to take less royalty than had been agreed upon. Distribution, the designer believed, was also fundamental in Esquire's troubles. He checked Iroquois accounts to see if they would market Knowles. International Silver was also contacted. A final suggestion that Home Decorators might rescue it was aborted just in time to save Wright's "face". He learned that Emily Post, not he, was their tableware authority. With no "takers", such a low volume would not support production costs. Wright could expect a decrease in volume until the end. And so it was. The end came in 1962.

Much has been said about the designs on the Knowles line, but the colors themselves were the real departure and reflected a distinct change from Wright's other work as well as from other dinnerware lines being sold at the time. Pastel colored in Beige, White, Pink, Yellow and Blue, they were originally a matte finish with an under-glaze, rubber-stamped pattern. The over-glaze gold stamping was part of the design and the gold was used in the back stamp which always named the pattern. Any Knowles with a high gloss was part of the effort to revitalize the line when all changes were being tried. The patterns were Seeds, Grass, Queen Anne's Lace, Snow Flower, Botanica and Solar. These are light, delicate abstract designs, very low profiled and truly hard to distinguish as the complaints reported. They were completely suited to the light body, however. Lids, as with the Iroquois line, were sold separately.

Again we notice the lack of national advertising, the absence of a distributor, and can only surmise the results of those influences. However, it can be stated that Russel Wright extended himself in every way to make a success of this line. He wrote that it was his "Company Set" at Dragon Rock, and in 1960, he wrote to the pottery in an effort to find replacements for his own use.

If he had trouble finding it, we can expect no less today. Unsuccessful as it was then, there is not a lot available for the collector. It is prized when found and when seen on the table reflects none of the criticisms aimed at it in 1958. If it is your choice, use it in pride. Russel Wright did.

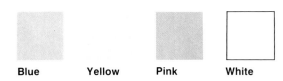

Blue   Yellow   Pink   White

On Pricing Knowles Esquire

Knowles collectors are fewer than are some of other lines, probably because there is less available to them. Certainly it is not because the line is of any less quality than the others. The volume made, I believe, is in proportion to the number who are looking for it today. It cannot be said that any one decoration is favored over another, all being welcomed equally. If there is a choice piece at this time, it would be the tea pot as it is prized by Russel Wright collectors and by tea pot collectors. Other rarities may present themselves as more of the Esquire patterns surface. If this line pleases you, be patient in your search for it is difficult but not impossible to find. Prices suggested include the lids combined with the tea pot and sugar as they obviously require them. The 9¼ " round serving bowl could be used without a cover and was therefore sold that way.

Knowles Esquire - All Patterns
Suggested Values

Dinner plate 10¼ "	$4.00-5.00
Salad plate 8¼ "	$3.00-4.00
Bread & butter plate 6¼ "	$2.00-3.00
Fruit/dessert 5½ "	$3.00-4.00
Soup/cereal 6¼ "	$4.00-5.00
Cup 7½ oz.	$4.00-5.00
Saucer	$2.00-3.00
Open oval serving bowl 12¼ "	$15.00-20.00
Round serving bowl 9¼ "	$10.00-12.00
Cover for above	$6.00-8.00
Oval platter 13"	$10.00-12.00
Oval platter 14¼ "	$12.00-15.00
Cream pitcher	$5.00-6.00
Covered sugar	$8.00-10.00
Salt	$4.00-5.00
Pepper	$4.00-5.00
2 qt. Pitcher	$20.00-22.00
Deep compote 7" x 12½ "	$22.00-25.00
Divided vegetable bowl	$12.00-15.00
Sauce boat	$8.00-10.00
Centerpiece - server 22"	$22.00-25.00
Tea pot	$25.00-30.00

Knowles Esquire shape

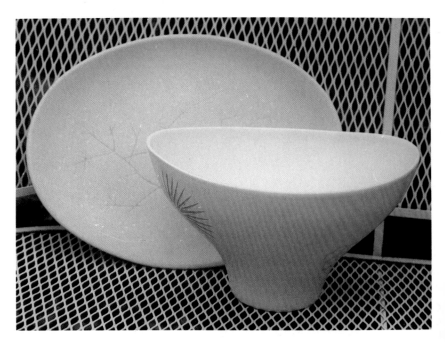

Snowflower 14½" platter; Solar deep compote.

Grass platter; Grass plates - 10¼" dinner, 8¼" salad, 6¼" bread & butter; Grass cup & saucer; Solar divided vegetable; Solar tea pot; Queen Anne's Lace 10¼" dinner plate; Grass round vegetable.

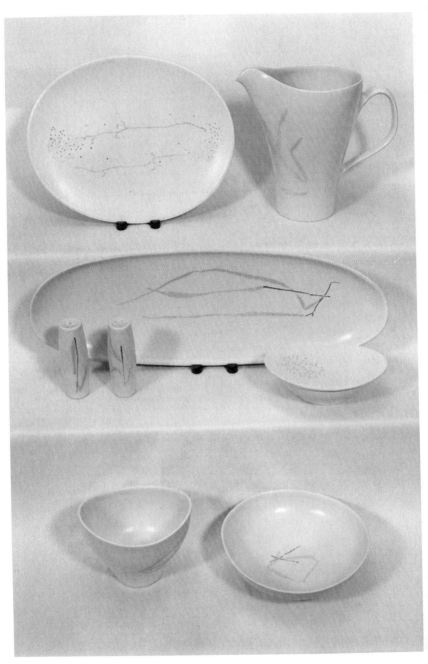

Queen Anne's Lace platter; Grass pitcher; Grass shakers; Grass centerpiece
server; Queen Anne's Lace covered sugar; Grass sauce boat; Grass round
vegetable.

Plastic Days

Up to this time, we have looked at the Russel Wright dinnerware lines in a time sequence and have seen the changes and development that occured within the area of his pottery lines. This seems as good a time as any to be reminded that while all the foregoing was happening, Wright was deeply involved in all other areas of the home furnishings field and in and around and between the dates we've mentioned, an avalanche of other products, almost all bearing the famous Wright signature, were introduced. American Modern became almost a cult with buyers searching for, and often achieving, a total Russel Wright look in their homes.

In 1945, the word "plastic" was new to most of us. This new material would change our lives in many ways.

Of course the new medium interested Russel Wright, and in 1944, he turned to The American Cyanide Company in New York which was testing a synthetic product which they had copyrighted as Melamine. During the advanced stages of their experimentation, they produced a pilot set, naming the material Melmac, the line Meladur, and used their resources to help the designer find a manufacturer for it. It is interesting that this project found few companies interested. However, after four years of search, General American Transportation Company agreed to produce the line with variations.

This prototype set the specifications for the multi-million dollar business that Melmac dinnerware was to become. The designer claimed the patent on the ware as he felt it to be the prototype for all Melamine dinnerware. American Cyanide felt they had developed it and had rights to it also. Legalistic correspondence followed in 1951 and American Cyanide was required to relinquish all rights to the newly named Meladur. Russel Wright was acknowledged as the sole owner of the line. General American agreed that they would use his name only with his approval and that each time it was used, it must be reviewed by Wright on the merit of each instance. Where it was allowed, his standard contract applied. Additionally, all advertising must be approved by the designer. In return they could produce what was called a "furnished set." In 1953 Wright relinquished, granted and sold to General all rights, title, and complete ownership of designs and all modifications in return for a lump payment of $15,000.00. General had the absolute right to use and sell. They could add to the line or modify it without his consent but when the existing stock was disposed of, they could no longer use his name. Added was the stipulation that if General ever sold the rights to the line, no one else could use his name. Sightings are reported where the signature is not present, reflecting the change in ownership reviewed here. Unsigned or differently signed items were made after 1951 and items which seem to be part of a set but do not have the signature are not Wright designed.

What I have been able to picture for you is in pink. It is surely safe to assume that other colors exist. The refined subtle shapes are pleasing and the Melmac is warm, not brittle. Clearly, it was an auspicious beginning for the new product.

By 1953 the wonder material was well accepted and many molders were rushing to use Cyanide's research in their own lines of Melmac. Northern Indistrial Chemical Company joined the rush in the most effective way they knew - by hiring Russel Wright to design a line to be called Residential, a full dinnerware line intended for home use. In 1957 however, there followed another troubled time for the designer. Northern, by that time, seemed to have confidence in their production and sales methods, especially in view of the fact that Residential was the best selling house- to-house dinnerware in the country. Their sales that year were $4,000,000.00. Russel, however, was dissatisfied with the sales results (and the amount of his royalties), feeling that Northern's sales efforts were not aggresssive as they should be. Northern responded by proposing the discontinuing production of Residential and the introduction of a new line by another designer. Wright countered by stating that if they did so, he would claim royalties on any line not designed by him that they produced. The dinnerware's own success seems to have been the factor that brought harmony to the two parties. It simply seemed that it was in their best interests to go along with Residential which had been awarded the Good Design Award by the Museum of Modern Art in 1953 and 1954. Northern was so impressed with its success that its one year guarantee was replaced with a ten-year warranty, complete with registration papers and certificate. Harmony was restored. Home Decorating Service was used to distribute a variant of Residential. The designer hoped for better sales from this change.

A new line, Flair, was introduced in 1959 and was immediately a best seller on its own merit. Melmac had arrived.

Residential differed from other synthetic dinnerware of its time. A great deal of experimentation had gone into achieving an almost translucent body with a cloud like speckled appearance. It was actually achieved by overlapping two colors, leaving the base coat showing through uncovered in spots. The trial and experimentation was no less on this new material than it had been on clay, and Russel Wright devoted a great deal of effort to produce a product which would be different, redesigning as he was asked. Tumblers were soon added as buyers took sugar lids off and made tumblers. Salesmen wanted to discontinue soup tops. Having forseen the time when plastics would be common-place, Wright wanted Residential to be a quality line. The use of metallic elements in combination with color added interest to the original colors of Sea Mist, Grey, Lemon Ice, Black Velvet (black with aluminum dust scatered in it) and Copper Penny (brown treated with copper dust). Other colors added later were White, Blue, and Salmon (red-orange). Residential was widely advertised, widely distributed, and is found today with more ease than are the other Wright Melmac or plastic lines. Different versions of the same item may present themselves to you as some items had a short production life, the designer being asked to redesign when needs arose. Needless to say, many items did double duty in such an informal usage.

Home Decorators, with the same manufacturing origins, was the "yes" answer to "Are there any more at home like you?" Made on the Residential shape and in the same pieces, it differed in that it was opaque - not clouded. It came in the late colors of White, Blue (turquoise), Orange-red and Pink. Naturalistic patterns, treated differently on each piece of the group, added to its informality and interest. Flair, another relative was executed on a different shape. You will find at least four Flair patterns: Ming Lace, Leaves, Nasturtium, and Cosmos. The design treatment was casual with each piece given a slightly different treatment. A saucer might have a bud; a cup, a leaf; a blossom in full bloom on the plate. The lack of uniformity added to the informal nature of the product.

As if all these lines were not enough, in 1957, Wright was experimenting with a new polyetheline material, Fortiflex for use in a dinnerware by the Ideal Toy Company. A different product altogether from Melmac, it was not waxy but soft and non-imitative of pottery. It had a fullness of form, making it (in the advertising jargon of the times), more compatable with ceramic ware. All the advertising trade aproaches that had worked so well with pottery were launched into being with this full line of dinnerware. Stack-ability, ease of serving, freezer-proof (a new approach), snap covers, ridges placed to avoid spillage - all were utilized. The ware was made in White, Turquoise, Yellow and Pink. Actually, today little Ideal-ware remains as it not as indestructable as it was claimed to be. It was soft enough to be considered flimsy and pieces almost squeezed in one's grasp. It won no awards and was produced for only a short time.

More successful by far was the line of plastic toy dishes, exact copies of American Modern, which Ideal made from a slightly harder plastic. We find them first offered for sale in the 1957 Sears Christmas catalogue. "Just like the Russel Wright set Mommy has" sets could be bought in service for four for $3.76. "Silver and glass" additions were not Russel Wright designs but the dishes themselves were accurately scaled, exactly colored miniatures of the Steubenville pieces. Two years later, one had the choice of a serving set for four or for six, but the colors were "off" from the original coloring. They appear again in 1961 but the last record I can find of them is in the Sears toy catalogue of 1964. In 1964 American Made Plastics Company in New York City assumed all Russel Wright designs done in plastic by Ideal. There is a great deal of interest in these tiny duplicates among those who search out Russel Wright designs. Collectors favor the originally colored items, however.

The plastic-Melmac polyetheline story is a complicated one, but as in the case of pottery, the man cannot be separated from his designs - and he was a leader in this new field right from the start. He had added integrity to a new material.

On Pricing Russel Wright Plastics

If the collecting of plastic dinnerware has a real place in the larger field of collecting, it is surely those who seek Russel Wright designs who have led the way. Those who collect Russel Wright dinnerware designs usually collect other of his wares and plastic has a real place in their priorities. On the other hand, plastic collecting is still relatively new and those who seek any of it are few, comparatively speaking. This affects values. The rule seems to be that if one wants it at *all*, he must be willing to pay a respectable price for it. Be aware, though, that much less plastic changes hands than do other materials, and so there is less demand. Use these prices very carefully as they reflect the sales of much less volume than other lines. More people are becoming interested and generally these prices are still holding at their first offered position with the exception of the toy dishes. Our listing is open-ended.

Meladur
Suggested Values

All Rare

Fruit 6 oz.	$5.00-6.00
Cereal 9 oz.	$6.00-8.00
Soup 12 oz.	$6.00-8.00
Salad 7¼"	$3.00-4.00
Dinner 9"	$3.00-5.00
Saucer	$1.00-2.00
Cup 7 oz.	$4.00-5.00
Bread & butter 5¾"	$3.00-4.00
Service plate 10"	$4.00-5.00
Compartmented plate 9½"	$6.00-7.00
Dessert plate 6¼"	$3.00-4.00

Home Decorator
Residential and Flair
Suggested Values

701 Cup	$3.00-4.00
702 Saucer	$1.00-2.00
703 Dinner plate	$3.00-4.00
704 Salad plate	$3.00-4.00
705 Bread & butter plate	$2.00-3.00
*706 Lug soup	$6.00-8.00
707 Fruit	$5.00-6.00
708 Oval vegetable bowl - shallow	$6.00-8.00
709 Oval vegetable bowl - deep	$8.00-10.00
710 Platter	$8.00-10.00
711 Creamer	$4.00-6.00
712 Sugar/cover	$7.00-9.00
713 Covered vegetable	$12.00-15.00
714 Divided vegetable	$8.00-9.00
715 Tumbler	$8.00-10.00
*716 Covered onion soup	$10.00-12.00 each piece

Add 25% for Black Velvet or Copper Penny. These are the hard-to-find colors.

*Rare

Pricing Ideal Toy American Modern Dishes

While plastic prices remain much the same as in 1981, these toy dishes are becoming more difficult to find. Most collectors are eager to put a set in their collection and prices reflect that demand. Prices range from $3.00 for a cup and saucer to $5.00 or $6.00 for a serving item. While usually found in sets, individual pieces are in demand to fill out sets not well cared for by the 1960's "Little Mommy". Her toy dishes were almost as fragile as their American Modern counterpart and are much more difficult to find today. Expect to find the correctly colored items at these prices. Off-color items are slightly less desirable. Boxed sets vary as to size and color but $45.00 - $50.00 is the average price on a complete set with the box in good condition.

Ideal Ware - Adult Kitchen Ware Suggested Values

All Rare

2 Sizes left-over bowls with cover	$6.00-8.00
Juice decanter	$5.00-6.00
Large water jug	$6.00-8.00
Butter dish and cover	$10.00-15.00
Tumblers - two sizes	$3.00-5.00
Freezing dish	$5.00-6.00
Salad and/or dessert plates	$2.00-3.00
Salad bowl	$6.00-7.00
Salad servers - fork & spoon	$7.00-8.00 pr.

MELADUR - HOME DECORATOR

Meladur Pink plates, cup & saucer, cereal, fruit; Home Decorator Bow Knot sauc
cup, divided vegetable, covered onion soup; Home Decorator Leaf dinner; F
vegetable; Home Decorator Bow Knot dinner and bread & butter plate.

RESITENTIAL

Dinner plate; 5-Piece place setting box; Covered vegetable; Bread & butter; Tumbler-sugar with cover; Platter, creamer, covered sugar; Cup - saucer, lug soup, fruit, round vegetable bowl; Off-colored cup.

FLAIR
Sugar; Platter, dinner plate, creamer; Patterned saucers & cup; Fruit, ova
vegetable, cup & saucer.

Residential in original boxed set.

IDEAL WARE
American Modern toy dishes in original box; From the collection of Bill
Strauss.

91

Glass, The Natural Companion

As early as 1945, Russel Wright had made drawings for a group of glass accessory items and had contracted with Century Metalcraft for their manufacturing. It is not known why Century did not produce, but by the next year (1947) the contract had been sold to American Crystal who agreed to take over the production. It was proposed as a companion line to American Modern. All crystal and probably paper stickered, it is unclear whether either of these firms ever produced it, but surely prototypes at least were made and it seems right to include the listing here. Possible items were punch sets, three sizes of tumblers - juice to Zombie, centerpiece bowl, salad plate, cup and saucer, cheese board, salad set, and tray and coaster. A handsome salad fork and spoon combining metal and glass has been found, and assuming it was part of the group, we may expect to find more.

During this early 1946 period, Raymor approved a somewhat smaller accessory line which was to have been made of bent glass by the Appleman Art Glass Company and intended to be companions to American Modern. The nature of bent glass limits the number of proposed items but they were to have included salad plates, candy dishes, fruit bowls and relish trays. Wright's association with Appleman lasted for about six years and while we have no examples or further descriptions, it seems very likely that this line was at least prototyped and that we may hope to find it.

A contract with Fostoria Glass Company in 1946 sent me on a search for those items. It was to be rewarding but disappointing. Wright had contracted with them for designs but no production was ever completed. David Dalzell, past president of Fostoria, explained to me that the glass was to have been a textured glass and Fostoria considered it to be unsanitary and impractical so none was made. Although disappointed, I was rewarded with a new understanding of contracts. I had previously felt them to be the final authority on the production of the many lines represented in the Syracuse files. I now had to evaluate such use and must question even a contract as proof of production.

What is certain however, is that in 1951, the American Modern dinnerware was complemented by a complete glassware grouping. Contrary to our first thinking, it is now known that this was made by Old Morgantown, a respected manufacturer of handmade glass. The first pieces were three tumblers: water, iced tea, juice; and stems: cocktail, wine, sherbet and goblet. A dessert dish was added for good measure. Later additions were a tall Pilsner, a double old fashioned glass and a chilling bowl with liner used to serve seafood cocktails or other foods requiring ice to keep chilled.

This crystal was made in complimenting colors of Coral, Seafoam, Chartreuse, Clear Crystal and what we have called Smoke. Early advertising names it Granite Grey and Smoke may have been a term used in later years.

The American Modern crystal was sticker labeled with no manufacturer's name. With the stickers removed it is somewhat difficult to distinguish in a glass crowd and collectors are often unsure of whether or not their tumblers are really Russel Wright tumblers. Generally, color is our best guide since shapes are so much the same. Even that principle is questionable when we get into the area of Smoke/Granite Grey. If you question authenticity, look to the dealer with whom you work. If he is familiar with all Russel Wright, he probably knows the real thing. If he claims this is his first, be cautious. It is difficult to identify.

More certain is the Pinch line done by Imperial as companion glassware to Iroquois Casual. Adding it at the time when Casual was restyled (1951), Imperial was to produce tumblers in three sizes - 14 oz., 11 oz. and 6 oz. It was appropriately named "Pinch" and was available in Verde, Seafoam, Smoke (the granite grey of the American Modern line) Pink (coral), Canteloupe (light amber) Chartreuse and Ruby (primary bright red). Interestingly, while all the others have appeared to collectors, I know of only one sighting of the Ruby and Canteloupe, and that came to me by chance. I was in the showroom of the Imperial Glass Company at a time when they were closing out many old things and found Verde among them. In a special grouping of things from their Research and Development Department were two Ruby tumblers and one of Canteloupe. Priced higher than the Verde and in this special section, it caused me to wonder if Imperial knew something collectors didn't. I asked, but it was at a troubled time in Imperials's life and no one remained who had the answer. Wright associates are surprised at this finding for Ruby and Canteloupe do not seem to be a part of their Imperial recall. The colors, with the exception of Canteloupe, are all listed in advertising and in Imperial sales literature, and the Syracuse papers attest to Canteloupe as being an accepted color. They have been found with polished and unpolished bottoms. Off-color sightings have been reported but most of these have been explained by lovely look-alikes made by Fostoria and Heisey. Some color experimentation by Imperial may have been done but even this would have resulted in small or insignificant examples.

Imperial also made three other tumblers of varying size in 1955 called Flair. They were to have been part of Russel Wright's contribution to the American Way project and so probably were short lived. Flaring out from a small base they were frosted and bubbly in texture and were called Seed glass. They could well be the glassware previously rejected by Fostoria. Crystal and pink as well as another color, of which I am uncertain, were made. Do not confuse this to be a companion to the plastic Flair dinnerware. I am fortunate to have found an example in Imperial's close-out sale. A recent correspondence from Imperial states that they made only tumblers in Seed glass. Be that as it may, advertising of that time period shows bowls and underplates.

In 1957, Russel Wright combined with The Bartlett Collins Glassware Company to produce a line of tumblers with a huge variety of decorations. Up to this point I have been unwilling to call "compromise" as others have done, but the Bartlett Collins line seems unexplainable in any other context. This glassware was to be sold in chain stores and variety stores and was to be priced low. The designer was warned that their customers demanded a constant change in the patterns offered and the rule was "the more gold, the better." A constant stream of designs resulted, each less typical of Wright designs than the other. Gay Nineties lamp poles, barber shop quartets, bustled ladies, bottles appropriately labeled scotch, rye or what have you, were all used. "Name your poison", "You can't take it with you", "If you drink don't drive". "Bottoms up" - and a host of other familiar phrases adorned them. Oranges and tomatoes fancy up water bottles and cookie jars and made "sets" when combined with tumblers. Among the better ones was a polka dot design in various sizes of colors and gold as well as one with a geometric theme.

Both of these more restrained patterns are pictured here. Sunburst was the name given to the geometric pattern and the dotted design was named Eclipse. The term seems apt when one considers the gold and colored dots overlapped. Astute Wright glass collectors have questioned other glassware with the same circles and colors which do not have the overlapping pattern. By remembering the name Eclipse and its implication, we can identify the Wright design. It seems reasonable that the unidentified pattern is a Russel Wright adaptation. Both patterns pictured came in Yellow, Turquoise, Green and Flamingo Pink - all combined with Gold. I would not rule out other colors. All are done on Bartlett Collins Oklahoma shape.

Never satisfied with quantity, Bartlett Collins moved on to newer ideas in short order, leaving the designer very little richer and almost exhausted with the sort of design this market required.

The Paden City glassware is discussed in the section on Highlights because glass dinnerware items were made as part of the table settings. You will recall that Paden City Glass Company closed before the end of the dinnerware line. The Yamato glass is included in the chapter concerning its dinnerware as it followed the same course.

On Pricing Glassware

What values one ascribes to the American Modern and Iroquois glassware lines is in direct proportion to where it is found and how it is recognized. If your area is like mine, you may well be the only one you know who recognizes and values it and it may come your way very reasonably. If, on the other hand, you find it in a knowedgeable dealer's shop, expect to pay from $15.00-20.00 for each piece, slightly more for the American Modern Pilsner and chilling bowl and a bit less for the dessert dish. The Iroquois Ruby and Canteloupe will be more expensive than other colors, if your findings parallel mine.

Imperial Flair and the better designed Bartlett Collins are still at almost garage sale prices in most areas but city shops have them priced at $6.00-8.00 each.

Glassware remains an area where great bargains are still to be found since so much goes unrecognized and, in addition, it has not yet become as popular as pottery or metal. Good fortune will be yours if you recognize it while others do not. Shape will help, but color will be your guide. Try to resist similar shapes in other colors.

OLD MORGANTOWN
AMERICAN MODERN GLASSWARE
Chartreuse iced tea glass; Coral water tumbler; Chartreuse dessert dish.

OLD MORGANTOWN
AMERICAN MODERN GLASSWARE
Seafoam chilling bowl; Chartreuse goblet; Grey sherbet; Chartreuse cocktail glass.

American Modern Glassware Brochure collector value $12.00-15.00.

IMPERIAL GLASS
Iroquois "Pinch"; Smoke 6 oz. tumbler; Ruby 14 oz. tumbler; Smoke 11 oz. tumbler.

A Look At Linen

Over a ten year period beginning in 1948, Russel Wright was to design for many fabric concerns in the country and several of those manufactured table linens of various materials - cotton and rayon as well as plastic.

His earliest work was with a group of cloths and napkins designed to be used with American Modern in 1948 and three different styles were produced by the New York firm of Leacock. A narrow banded plaid was made in Coral on Grey, Seafoam on Yellow and Chartreuse on Yellow. An abstract design with geometric lines of various widths came in Chartreuse on Grey, Grey on Grey, Coral on Grey and Chartreuse on Yellow. A pencil line design called Brush Strokes completed the line and was available in Grey on Yellow, Seafoam on Grey, Grey on Grey and Chartreuse on Yellow. All were sold with solid colored napkins and came in three sizes - 54 x 54, 54 x 72 and 63 x 80. They were made only until 1952.

In direct competition with the Leacock American Modern line was one produced in 1950 for Simtex Mills called Simtex Modern. This is the bold block symetrical plaid which is most readily identified. Made of cotton and rayon and using the same colors as Leacocks, it also came in the same sizes. In 1951 Simtex Modern was the winner of the Museum of Modern Art's award for the best design. An interesting advertising ploy told the buyer that the napkins should be called "matkins" and used either as place mats or napkins.

During this same time frame, Patchogue Mills made two woven cloths, also of geometric design and much advertising promoted the fact that they were woven on Nottingham looms.

Several plastic lines were to have followed as that material evolved in a way that could be adapted to table use. Cohen Hall, Marx and Company were early producers of plastic tablecloths and mats in 1946. In 1948 Frank and Saden was permitted to use the Wright signature on mat and napkin sets. The Aristocrat Leather Company made the same product in 1951 as did Comprehensive Fabrics.

The last producer of vinyl cloths and napkins for whom Wright worked was The Hedwin Corporation in 1953. The association was brief but eventful. The designer believed Hedwin was too aggressive in its manufacturing and selling, taking parts of his designs and adapting them to their own product. They used his colors on other wares without his approval and did not secure the services of a national distributor, the use of which he favored. Additionally their price was too high! With such serious objections by the designer and bound by his contract, Hedwin was forced to remove the objectionable merchandise from all stores and then to replace it with the approved full line. From that time he not only drew royalties on all sales in which his lines were involved, he also became known as their color consultant - for a year. The fiasco resulted in slow sales and the line was soon dropped.

Collectors today will be fortunate if they find a cloth or napkin set of any material with the label still attached, therefore identification is a problem. It will be easier for those who are familiar with the early American Modern colors, however, as with concentration on those colors combined with a geometric plaid or pattern, the search may be fruitful. These cloths stand out as importantly and obviously as do the metal or ceramic items. Lucky will be the one who makes a "warehouse find" of all the returned Hedwin sets. Most collectors would be happy to be even that close to a Russel Wright table cover.

On Pricing Linens and Plastic Table Covers

So little of Russel Wright's linen and plastic comes to us in good condition that values are not as high as one might expect. Demand is conditioned by the fact that these items, even in mint condition, cannot be used as much nor as often as can a piece of metal or pottery. Also, usage may not have faded them, but shapes once laundered never seem pristine again. You should not expect to pay more than $25.00 for an item of this sort but if you do find a piece with the label intact, treasure it. Most have been used and abused.

Chase Chrome ice pail; #127 Relish dish 13¼", false bottom for ice, glass insert; Early fruit bowl; Simtex tablecloth. Linen cloth from collection of Ted Haun.

Spice

FOR YOUR TABLE

Stoneware by Duncan & Miller

Bold, wonderful tablecloths, seasoned to a modern's taste for verve and color! Simtex woven of rayon and cotton with a deep touch-inviting texture. They have the look of fine tweeds—would be absolutely perfect in ranch or modern setting. Completely washable, guaranteed fast colors, with a rich hand that actually improves with laundering. 52″ x 52″, 52″ x 70″ cloths.

Simtex Matkins (can be used as napkins or mats) in solid color-accents, 12″ x 18″.
For store names write to: Simtex Mills, Division of Simmons Co., 40 Worth Street, New York 13, N. Y.

Simtex Modern, chosen by the Museum of Modern Art for outstanding Good Design

Simtex

MODERN
DESIGNED BY

Russel Wright

SIMTEX COVERS MORE TABLES THAN ANY OTHER MAKER IN AMERICA

Simtex Modern Table Cloth Advertisement. Circa 1950.

The Bauer Experiment

In none of the Russel Wright affiliations was there more care in planning the line and its marketing than was taken with the Bauer Pottery Company of Atlanta. In 1945, with his first pottery work after American Modern, the designer agreed to submit designs for art pottery wares and Bauer could supervise, criticize and make a final selection of the twenty items to be produced. The combined services of Bauer's ceramic engineers and Wright's dependable ceramist, Doris Coutant, were to be used and the designer agreed to help with sales literature, advertising, promotion and marketing in general. The items not selected were to be Wright's property, but he agreed that if the Bauer line was placed on the market by March 3, 1946, he would not place another art pottery line on the market or cause another line to go into production for a year. As though those terms were not restrictive enough, he further agreed that he would not work with another art pottery as long as Bauer's sales on his line held at $150,000.00 annually. In return, Bauer could not make shapes similar to his, nor could they use his glazes on their other ware without his consent. If that consent were given, he would receive 2% royalty on those items. His own work was to receive 4% royalty on first quality items, a 2% royalty on "off selection" which were to be sold at a discount. He was to receive a monthly statement of his account and $6,000.00 was to be paid monthly from July 1, 1945, to continue as long as the line was sold. This payment schedule gave him returns while the line was being designed but would later be in addition to his royalties. He had the right to examine their books at any time and if they ever found themselves in bankruptcy, his designs could not be sold and would revert to him.

With such elaborate contractural planning, neither party appeared to be prepared for the troubled times that followed. Shape-wise the items were ingeniously contrived to accomplish the effect of rocks, the habitat of growing flowers and colors were to be achieved that would add to that quiet background. Lines were curved and flowing to allow sharpness and contrast to appear in the flowers themselves. Colors were to have been subdued so that the flower colors would always be stronger than that of the container. Such a simplistic effect proved difficult to achieve. Doris was sent to Atlanta and for a year, the mail was constantly reporting unsuccessful attempts to accomplish the glazes Russel Wright required and over a thousand trials were run. Even Wright threw up his hands from time to time telling Doris and the Bauer engineer to "use their best judgment", but most often a postscript with specific instructions was added. Formula changes were tried and rejected and Bauer warned him that the consistancy and uniformity he expected was not possible with the type glaze he desired. Color variations, they said, would inevitably result. With this situation still existing, the approved designs were sent to the New York showing in January of 1946. Almost all was second quality with glaze runs, drips and unevenness. Bubbles of glaze burst open on what should have been sleek surfaces. Out of Bauer's 600 accounts, not one order was received. Obvious imperfections in the glazes were discreetly ignored as the reason for its rejection and it was said to be "too modern, too much of an oddity." Perhaps some buyers felt the imperfections were intended, as a few orders were received later.

Herbert Brushche, President of Bauer at the time, tells me that production lasted only about six months and that if it had continued, the glaze runs would have destroyed their kilns.

The items which were approved were standard in some instances, innovating in others and include:

Flower pot and saucer 4½″
Oval vases 7″ and 10½″
Round vase 6¼″
An off-centered bowl
Jardiniere bowl 7½″
Centerpiece bowl 17″
Mantelpiece bowl with candle holder ends 23¾″
Various Japanese garden dishes
Vase 10″ with ribs in bottom to secure flowers
Vase covers - frogs to hold stems separate
Servers - a strange item to find here
Wall vase 8¾″
Pillow vase 8½″
Corsage vase 5″
Table vase $8^{3}/_{8}$″ and $9^{1}/_{8}$″
Lamp
Bulb bowl 11″
Floor vase 22″
Melon jardiniere 8½″

This listing does not include ash trays but at least two are known to exist. While the entire listing was an accepted one, with such abortive production, it is questionable that all were produced. Variations seem likely in view of the experimentation. Certainly none of it was made in large numbers.

Glaze colors approved after these protracted experiments were to have been many and may include: Jonquil Yellow, Dirty Yellow, Lemon Yellow, Atlanta Brick (Terra Cotta), Cinnamon, Bronze, Pale Moss Green, Celadon Green, Green Metal, Dark Moss Green, Potlach Green, Raymor Turquoise, Aqua, True Blue, Black, Bubbly White and Glossy White. All pieces were to be made in all colors, some in combinations of colors with different inside glaze treatments. The combinations which could have resulted are staggering and our original twenty pieces could have expanded to a huge line.

Made to be sold for $1.25 to $10.00, they were to be marked with the signature and the Bauer name molded, stamped or stickered. Collectors find them, in some cases, unmarked because stickers were removed, as well as with barely discernable marks where glazes have filled in the molded writing. Some bottoms are glazed, other show the clay body and in some cases one can see the almost 1″ thick glaze that was often used. Like frosting, it covers but unevenly. It is difficult to believe this to be machine-made pottery, but that fact stands.

The Bauer experiment was one that surely would have been tried again had the designer's interest not turned to other avenues. It was a market he'd met with in which he'd found rejection and the option of "another art ware line" was a speculation he returned to often in his plans. He did not take defeat lightly and his confidence in his ability to correct the flaws in the Bauer line remained with him for a long time.

On Pricing Bauer Art Pottery

In spite of its rejection in 1946, collectors today prize a piece of Russel Wright Bauer very highly. It is all to be considered rare and the collector accepts the imperfect pieces with the perfect pieces, pleased to have an example in his collection. No value difference seems dependent upon perfection. Values seem instead to be based on the size of the piece; while small items are priced at $50.00, larger ones are bringing $200.00. These Bauer items are the really important pieces in the collections of many who seek Russel Wright designs and there are not nearly enough to satisfy their appetite. Expect prices to go higher in the future.

Blue ash tray; Black vase 10½", Flower pot 4½".

Pillow vase; Oval vase 7″; Ash tray; Centerpiece bowl; Mantelpiece bowl.

What Might Have Been

In 1964 the trade magazine *China Glass and Lamps* ran a small announcement of few details covering a new Russel Wright dinnerware ensemble called Theme Formal and Theme Informal. In 1981 my research on this stopped with that announcement and might have ended there if, in the fall of that year in New York City, I'd not been shown some white porcelain demi-cups and saucers marked with the Russel Wright signature, Yamato Porcelain and Designed in Japan. This finding sent me back to the Wright files at Syracuse with a far longer look at his contracts and the folios they represented. Under Schmid International, I found "Dining accessories of various materials"-such a simple title for what was to describe a very long line of coordinated porcelain, stoneware, lacquer ware, glass and wood. For details I turned to those who had worked with the designer and I soon had photocopies describing this unusual line. It had not been overlooked in our study; it had been a line not produced (and you can imagine that a list of unproduced things would be a ridiculous point of reference.) It had been completely designed, however, with Yamato in Japan, the manufacturer; Schmid International, the importer; and Raymor, the distributor.

In 1965 these companion lines were presented at the New York Gift Show and to the surprise of involved parties, were completely rejected by the China buyers. Orders were too few to go into production and plans for it were abandoned at once. The buyers found themselves facing a slump in the sales of dinnerware and this new "return to elegancy" seemed totally unmarketable in the climate of the 60's. It was geared to the young, ready-for-anything segment of society which had so often hailed Russel Wright as its touchstone, but the young people of the 1960's were making their own statement with new and different priorities. Along with this disregard for the elegant came a rejection of materialism. By no means were all young people in the same mold, but they shared certain characteristics and one of these was a return to basics and a simple life. Their philosophy was, as his, concerned with average people's needs, but theirs was concerned with social changes more elemental than his. He believed they were the "New Elegant" interested in travel, gourmet food, and gracious aspects of dining and that they would prefer to serve with flair and formality. He had read them very wrongly, not an uncommon mistake in those times. Perceptive buyers, finding that the whole of the home furnishing industry had lost their young market with its usual large appetite for accumulating, were super cautious and recognized on sight that these new lines were completely out of touch. Some few pieces found their way out of showrooms into early collections and they represent what little we have found today. None was sold and only the prototypes were made. It is even questionable as to whether the entire line was prototyped in its complete color range. Enough has surfaced in shops and museums to interest the collector. If sets are impossible to acquire, some examples have been offered and these lead to questions as to what would have been available and what it would have been like.

The two concepts, Theme Formal and Theme Informal were separate, not made to match, but designed as an ensemble to complement each other and to establish a grouping to cover any dining mood. Theme Formal was a true, fine porcelain with more than a trace of Oriental influence, but with a distinctive 50's look also.

What has been seen is of a soft white sheen, with elongated soft curves and loopy finials for handles. It is the most conservative line Wright developed and culminates the Oriental suggestions found in his redesigned Iroquois, Knowles and Flair lines. Sophisticated, this Theme combined with dramatic black or Chinese red lacquerware and opalene glassware to form a completely coordinated look. The effect was totally formal, delicate and rich. Examples which may be found include: dinner, salad, bread and butter plates, cups and saucers in regular and after dinner size, tea pot and coffee pot, two platters, a covered vegetable bowl and a covered casserole, fruit bowls, coupe soup and cream soup and a sauce boat as well as a baker. To my knowledge, only the white has been found, but planning included a "spaced white on grey double dot pattern." The lacquerware, examples of which I have photocopies, only recently has come to my attention but it included a place plate, salad-dessert plate, a salad serving bowl and salad servers. The glassware was unquestionably the loveliest glassware of all he designed. Of opalescent glass, it shaded from white at the sham base to a tapered top of opaline self tint. It was neither stem nor tumbler, but a beautiful combination of both. This glassware, even by itself, is a miracle of his imagination. Four sizes were to be made: an 8 oz. goblet, a 12 oz. highball, a 5 oz. wine and a 3 oz. liquor. Harmony of detail was elegantly achieved in Theme Formal's porcelain, lacquer and glass.

Even Theme Informal, the stoneware counterpart of Formal, was too structured for the 60's market. Sturdily shaped, as the material and name suggest, it was also Orientally inspired but more casually so. Its counter-theme was a balance for Formal and it was hoped that owners would use both, for their separate and appropriate occasions.

Informal was planned in two colors: Ember, a black-brown with orange flecks, or Dune, a mottled sand tone with the heavy drip over-glaze in white. Only Dune has been seen and it is possible that only that was prototyped. The stoneware line was to be smaller with double duty suggested as informal usage would have it. Items were dinner plates, bread and butter plates, cups, saucers, and a mug, a stacking vegetable server, sugar and creamer, a soup/cereal dessert bowl and a casserole. As had been done with the Paden City Highlight line, glass items were to have been used with the ceramic pieces. They were optic blown glass with more conventionally shaped tumblers in three sizes, a salad plate and a dessert bowl as well as a stacking cream and sugar set. All these were to be in the buyers' choice of amber or smoke green. Only one example has come to my attention, and it is pictured here by courtesy of the Brooklyn Museum. Less distinctive than the Formal glassware, it may be going unrecognized.

Wooden bowls, finished naturally to show the wood grain, completed the total effect of Theme Informal.

Rejection of these lines was a discouragement to Wright, who had put a good bit of time, as well as a good measure of his personal taste, into their conception. It was a difficult experience for him. He should not be seen as licking his wounds, but he *was* wounded, and the therapy of the woods at Garrison and his life at Dragon Rock were his comfort. He did not return again to the dinnerware market place. The "Midas Touch" seems to have failed him in the end.

On Pricing Theme Formal and Theme Informal

With rarity so obvious a feature, prices on these few items have been high, and I would suggest that one use the Paden City prices as a base and go up from there in pricing. At the same time, such rarity probably precludes the collection of a "set" and so demand is not as prevalent. These are lines of which the advanced collector would be willing to pay a premium but for which the average user would find little value beyond the acquisition of an example and he might be unwilling to spend the high price which is usually asked. As with all else, one must define one's own collecting and in this case, make an individual jugdement on the value of your collection.

THEME FORMAL
8 oz. Goblet; 3 oz. liquor; 5 oz. wine.

THEME FORMAL
After dinner cup and saucer.

THEME INFORMAL
Glass tumbler, gift of Russel Wright to The Brooklyn Museum. Shown here by permission.

THEME FORMAL
Porcelain bowls. Credit Steve Tucker.

Rounding It Out

Silver flatware with square handles and circle bowls was an early experiment with flatware prototyped but never produced. Handsomely designed, it is unfortunate that more pictures of it were made than were made of the set itself. Only one is known to exist. It belongs to Russel's daughter, Ann.

A further disappointment for collectors is the fact that only one style of Hull stainless steel was made. Contrary to the thinking of many writers and collectors, Hull's flatware was made in 1953 to accompany the Paden City - Justin Tharaud - Highlight line. A different set to be used with American Modern does not exist. The Highlight stainless steel is much less severe than the prototyped silver with handles, more contoured and bowls not so exactly circular. Tarnish-proof with a soft brushed-satin finish, it is perhaps a bit light in weight, but its contoured lines makes for ease in holding. The knives are pinched at the point where blade and handle meet, spoons and forks not showing the pinch. This Highlight line was a complete one: knife, butter knife, fork, salad fork, tablespoon, tea spoon and iced tea spoon. A large serving spoon, slotted spoon and cake server were also available, and it is possible other serving items may exist which we have not seen.

Predictably, Hull stainless joined the other award winning Wright designs when the Museum of Modern Art singled it out at once for its Good Design Award. Macy's in New York City introduced Highlight and it won immediate acceptance. Carrying a life-time guarantee, a six-piece set was introduced for $6.95. The chest to hold it sold for $7.95.

During the production time of this ware, Hull moved its facilities to Japan and, for that reason, it comes with two different marks. That made in America has the Wright signature, the words "Hull Stainless" and a patent number. Those made in Japan are the exact same product but the mark adds the word Japan. Regardless of manufacturing origin, collectors find no difference in desirability. Both Japanese and American items may be used interchangeably as they are identical.

At a time when the Scandanavians dominated the stainless flatware trade in this country, Wright's work was in competition with theirs. A similarity in line may be explained by the fact that this Scandanavian look was the "new look" of the day - another departure from the traditional. It was another instance, seen often, of a style developing and designers going in the same direction with no desire to imitate, but rather to incorporate the best influences.

Highlight knives are seldom found with a Hull stainless set. Hollow handles were in fashion in the 1950's and stainless steel purchasers often substituted another knife to go with their Russel Wright stainless steel. As a result, broken sets are usually found today. Knives may be the hardest items to find to complete a set, and may be, for that reason more costly than other pieces.

Disappointing as it has been to find the Hull set numbered at one instead of the two we'd formerly believed to exist, it is even more disappointing to find "empty contracts" on other flatware. A contract with Englishtown Cutlery would have produced a plastic handled ware much different from that which we find on the market today. Additionally, a contract with National Silver which would have produced three lines of stainless steel also resulted in no production. Only a prototyped silver tea/coffee set belonging to Herbert Honig is believed to exist in spite of extensive design work which Wright did for them. It adds up to a loss for collectors.

On Pricing Stainless Flatware

Russel Wright stainless steel is most difficult to find. The modest price it has carried is not a rejection of the demand but rather that not enough has become available to establish prices. At the present, items are priced from $5.00 to $10.00 with serving pieces, knives, and iced tea spoons at the higher range. These prices apply to the Hull lines, American or Japanese made. Be wary of stainless steel ware made in Japan and marked to suggest it is Russel Wright or American Modern but not displaying the signature. No Hull stainless carried the term American Modern. The Hull Japanese product as well as the American Hull bears the designer's name in script. I have been told of at least two other lines, Japanese made, which collectors were led to believe were the Russel Wright line; you should not be misled by terms that suggest the real thing. The National Silver items have no established pricing as none have surfaced.

HIGHLIGHT STAINLESS STEEL
Slotted spoon; Cake lifter; Serving spoon; Table knife, butter knife, fork, salad fork, tablespoon, teaspoon, iced tea spoon.

Even More

There was more - much, much more if the total production amount is considered, including interior work in homes and businesses, as well as product work. We list here the remaining tabletop things which concern us. Some may be empty contracts with no production, but even in such cases, prototypes may have resulted and we should consider anything as possible.

The Southerland Paper Company produced paper tableware for which the claim was made that the new paper goods were not of picnic variety, but intended for home use. Dated 1950-1961, there were six decorative lines "prettied up" for supermarket sales.

Ravenswood Aluminum Company held a contract in 1955, and a large line was submitted for their approval. For some reason which defies understanding, the aluminum pieces when finished, turned out to be brass. Upset, the designer asked for an additional fee if this was marketed. None has come to my attention and it well may be that the parties agreed to drop the project.

Aluminum Manufacturing Goods marketed a stove-to-table accessory line under their trade name of Mirro in 1945. None has been found.

In 1947 the Appleman Art Glass Works in New Jersey, was permitted to use his name on certain "sets" which he designed including a salad set and a dessert set among others. These were probably paper-labeled and will be difficult to identify if they exist.

Bowes Industries of Chicago, another paper goods manufacturer, produced a Russel Wright line of table goods from 1950 to 1951.

Strangely, the Thermo tree and well server which Cornwell Corporation of Boston, Massachusetts, made from 1958-1961, has not been found. His name should identify it. Advertising confirms its existence.

The Duraware Corporation of New York was the last manufacturer of thermoplastic Russel Wright serving items. They came at a late date - 1964 - and were signed, but even my plastic authority, B. A. Wellman has none in his collection. They should be marked if indeed they were produced.

The S.S. Sarna line of 20 pieces basketry wood and aluminum made in 1957 may yet be found.

The unsigned Shenango institutional ware dated 1944 may rest with the Sterling line in old restaurant supply houses.

At least two Silex coffee makers, both marked but probably tagged, have Wright design. These date from 1942.

The 1947 contract with Lodge Electric Company for a popcorn popper, unsigned, may well be the spun aluminum popper that collectors seek and which was a part of the Wright Accessories line.

Very few of these sundry items have surfaced, and we know of them by reading through his contracts and files. Be aware that production is uncertain. Those of you who clip old magazine advertisements may well be the first to identify some of this, and I ask that you share any new information you find. In the meantime, may the thrill of the chase reward all of you with your collecting, and may your pleasure be increased by knowing the facts behind the find.

Mary's Contribution

It would be wrong to leave a discussion of Russel Wright's work without reference to his wife, Mary. She was born Mary Einstein of the wealthy, intellectual and socially prominent California family, all of whom objected to the marriage. The couple had eloped in the face of open opposition. Mary brought to her marriage many obvious resultant advantages which were to be valuable to Russel Wright's career, but none were more important than the partnership of love and work which the couple established at once.

In Russel's earliest design work, Mary threw herself into every position that needed a hand to promote her husband's work, establishing a pattern that prevailed for the rest of her life. Her social connections proved helpful in those early days and contract work came Russel's way, in large part, because Mary was able to open doors and present his designs. Later, when they were in the budding spun aluminum days, Mary took charge of organizing the downstairs manufacturing facilities, set up a model sales program, complete with hand drawn advertisement copy, and went out to meet accounts. In theory, this left Russel the freedom to exercise his artistic abilities, a position he would endlessly seek. By 1936 the future appeared promising, and with Mary's financial backing they were able to join with Irving Richards, by then an "old" business partner, and organize what was later to become the Raymor Company. Mary and Mr. Richards were to own the voting stock and Russel was to design for Raymor exclusively for a five-year period. His work was to include many of the items we have discussed here. Mary and Irving Richards, with control of the company, paid profits as dividends and business decisions were made jointly. Mary was ever cautious in her husband's behalf. At this point, we must recognize that these decisions of sound judgement demonstrated her adventurism in finding new marketing methods. Together she and Richards wrote a new chapter in merchandising and many of Russel Wright's accomplishments were due to the concepts formulated and put into practice by his wife and friend. They were writing the "text book" principles of business to which Russel referred all his working life. At the end of the contract period, the Wrights sold their interests to Richards who continued to market these Wright-designed items (as well as those of other designers) and Russel received royalties as his payment. His design firm, Russel Wright Associates, continued. Both the Wrights came to have second thoughts on that sales decision because the Steubenville American Modern dinnerware went on to such a long outstanding sales period and they felt they had sold too quickly. Surely at the time it seemed wise, and in retrospect, one must consider that Raymor royalties were substantial to the designer until the very end.

Mary was a part of all Russel did during those halcyon days. She went to department stores and gave demonstrations, made speeches, was pictured with Russel in promotional advertising as well as in news accounts. Mary sold Russel with style. She promoted American Way designers work as well as his, and filled herself into his works wherever there was a need. Her collaboration with him in writing *A Guide to Easier Living* clearly shows that she espoused his creed as much as she promoted his business.

Aside from all that has been said, Mary Wright was a creative designer herself. Her Country Gardens dinnerware line, the product which we most identify her with, was a personal heartbreak. Designed for the Bauer Pottery Company in Atlanta, it was undergoing glaze trials there and in Los Angeles during 1946, while Russel's artware line was having some troubling days. Doris Coutant, his ceramist, was working on both lines in California and there is no doubt that Russel sketched some ideas for Mary's consideration during that time. The correspondence gives evidence. Doris would write, giving details of glaze experiments on Country Gardens and Russel would send back a letter telling her that this was none of his concern - that it was his wife's project. Then would follow specific instructions and answers to questions and the letter would end with "Please refer your questions to Mrs. Wright in the future as this is her affair." Obviously, their creative lives were as close as were their other interests. Country Gardens was shown at the Atlanta Housewares show on May 12, 1946, and buyers were few. All considered it an attractive line, but over-priced. The line which would have been made in Green, Brown, Pink and Beige seemed ended. Bauer claimed that their own costs could not reflect a better retail price, but Mary continued to pursue methods of production which she felt Bauer could adopt. The company remained firm, however, and their rejection was total. This came at the time when her illness of cancer was diagnosed and must have been a hard time for this young woman who had given so freely of herself to the work of others. After her death Russel gave one of her relatives the right to produce Country Gardens, but even that effort never achieved fulfullment. Prototyped examples have been found.

In addition to Country Gardens, Mary worked in the American Way program as a designer and she and Raymond Lowey were the designers for Everlast Metal Products, producing a hammered aluminum line of drinking and buffet accessories. She also designed and marketed at least one grouping of table linens centered on the garden theme - a kitchen garden, a fruit garden and a sea garden. All were more conventional than her husband's linen lines, but all were tastefully done. She is also credited with a desk and smoking accessory line of laminated leather, with fruit and sea motifs. Handsome snail bookends and fruit-shaped cigarette lighters exemplify this small line, sold by Wright Accesories and listed only as "other artists work especially selected by Russel Wright." In his furniture line, the blonde maple and mahogany terms were her concept.

If Russel Wright played a major role in design work, Mary Wright was the minor theme, always supportive, always complementary, ever present. Her death in 1952 was not unexpected, but the void it left in his personal and working life was never filled. In talking to family, friends and associates, I heard the same phrase over and over - "Mary adored him".

Skillet/server 12″ x 16″; Hinged lid casserole; Decanter 8″; Sugar - Spoon as cover; Dinner plate; Bread and butter plate; Platter type bowl 12″ x 6″; Soup bowl; Cup and saucer; Individual butter plateau 1½″; Butter plateau 6″. All items from the collection of Jack Williams. All very rare. No price established.

Potpourri

Bartlett Collins Eclipse ice bowl and tumblers; Mary & Russel's *Guide to Easier Living*; Ideal Toy plastic coffee pot; Iroquois cup handle variant; Iroquois gravy with ladle-slot; Bartlett Collins Flair glass with amber liquid; Ideal Toy covered vegetable; Ideal Toy creamer; Gravy with underliner; Sugar.

NOTE: Iroquois cup handle here is much like #5 shown in Iroquois section. This is a 702 cup and believed to be earliest handle.

Spun aluminum cheese board; Iroquois patterned creamer; Bauer vase; Iroquois sauce pan from Cook-ware line; Residential cup handle variant; Ideal ware butter dish; Spun aluminum punch set; Sterling coffee bottle.

Chronology

1904	Born April 3 in Lebanon, Ohio
1921-22	Student at Cincinnati Academy of Art
1922-24	Law student at Princeton
1923	Attended Columbia School of Architecture
1924-31	Engaged in Stage and Costume Design
1927	Married Mary Einstein
1930	Established his own factory for the production of first metal informal serving pieces, Russel Wright Incorporated, New York City
1930-31	Irving Richards and Wright started working relationship
1930-31	Experimentation and production of spun aluminum
1935	Russel Wright Incorporated changed to Russel Wright Accessories
1935	Klise Woodenware made Oceana
1935	Approximate date of Plantene production
1936	Approximate date of Chase Chrome work
1938	Designed American Modern dinnerware
1939	Steubenville Pottery agreed to produce American Modern
1938-39	Attended New York University School of Architecture
1939	Joined with Irving Richards to form Raymor. Exclusive distribution rights for 5 years on home furnishing designs
1939	Set up his own design office
1940-41	American Way products shown in department stores
1941	American Modern received the American Designers Institute award for the best ceramic design of the year
1941	War halted production of most metal items
1942	Silex coffee makers designed
1944	Shenango restaurant ware designed
1944	American Cyanide prototyped Meladur
1944	Raymor exclusive contract expired
1945	Bauer art pottery produced
1945	Glass work began with Century Metalcraft
1945	Aluminum Manufacturing Goods designed Mirro - a stove-to-table accessory line
1946	Iroquois Casual introduced
1946	Chase Chrome contract expired
1946	Cohen Hall Marx and Company designed plastic tablecloths and mats
1946	Mary Wright Country Gardens shown at Atlanta trade show
1946	Appleman Art Glass contracted to do bent glass items
1947	Englishtown Cutlery designed plastic handled flatware - contract signed
1947	American Crystal assumed glass contract from Century Metalcraft
1947	Popcorn popper produced by Lodge Electric Company
1948	Paden City Highlight introduced
1948	Leacock produced American Modern linens
1948	Frank & Saden table linens designed
1949	Sterling dinnerware produced
1950	Simtex Mills produced Simtex modern linens
1950	Herbert Honig joined firm as Business Manager

1950	American Modern Black Chutney and Cedar Green added to palette
1950	Sterling institutional ware discontinued
1950-51	Bowes Industries designed paper table goods
1951	Aristocrat Leather and Comprehensive Fabrics produced plastic table coverings
1951	Imperial Glass Company manufactured glassware to accompany Iroquois Casual
1951	General American Transportation produced Meladur
1951	Harker White Clover introduced
1951	Paden City White and Green added to palette
1951	*Guide to Easier Living* published by Simon and Schuster
1951	Received Home Fashions League "Trail Blazer" award for upholstery fabric and table service design
1951	American Modern line enlarged
1951-52	President of the Society of Industrial Designers
1951	Simtex Modern linens won Museum of Modern Arts award for best design
1951	Patchoque Mills given contract for geometric pattern woven linens
1951	American Modern Glassware produced by Old Morgantown
1951-52	Iroquois redesigned and new colors added
1951	Highlight won 1951 Museum of Modern Art Home Furnishing award and Trail Blazer award by Home Furnishings League
1952	Leacock American Modern linens discontinued
1952	Museum of Modern Art awarded Harker White Clover its "Good Design" award
1952	Mary Wright's death
1953	Paden City Snow Glass discontinued, pottery items substituted, additions and redesigns
1953	Wright sold Meladur rights to General American Transportation
1953	Hull produced stainless steel flatware to accompany Highlight
1953	Hull stainless steel won "Good Design" award from Museum of Modern Art
1953	Northern Indusrial Chemical contracted with Wright to design Residential
1953	Hedwin Corporation designed vinyl table coverings
1953-54	Residential won "Good Design" Award from Museum of Modern Art both years
1954	Home Decorating Service named to market a variant of Residential
1954	National Silver Company contracted designs flatware and various metal serving items
1955	Ravenswood Aluminum asked for design contract
1955	Knowles Esquire line introduced
1955	Canteloupe and Glacier Blue introduced as new American Modern colors
1955	Assigned by I.C.A. to develop native handicrafts for local and export use in Cambodia, Taiwan and Vietnam
1955	Approximate date of discontinuation of Paden City Highlight
1955	Approximate date of discontinuation of Harker White Clove
1955	Imperial Glass Company made Flair tumblers
1956	Seafoam, Chutney and Cedar dropped from regular American Modern line

1957	Bartlett Collins Glass Company, produced large line of decorated tumblers and bar-ware
1957	Ideal ware produced in polyethylene line
1957	SS-Sarna contract for 20 pieces of basketry, wood and aluminum
1957	Ideal Toy dishes produced
1958	Advisor on merchandising and selling in the wood and basketry industry in Japan
1958	Cornwell Corporation made small metal and wood table accessory line
1959	Flair added to Northern Industrial Chemical's line
1959	Patterned Iroquois added
1959-61	Southerland Paper made paper tableware
1960	Involved with U.S. Park System and Nature Conservancy in ecological programs for public lands
1962	Knowles discontinued Wright's designs on Esquire shape
1964	Duraware Corporation designs thermoplastic serving items
1964	American Made Plastics Company assumed Ideal line
1965	Yamato Theme Formal and Informal shown at New York gift show
1965	Iroquois line phased out by mid-1960's
1965	Polynesian drawing placed in Sterling files
1967	Closed Russel Wright Associates Design Studio
1976	Russel Wright's death was announced

Sources

Faced with the addition of a bibliography to this work, I am hard pressed. The Russel Wright papers, which he gave to Syracuse University on his death, have been and remain the chief source of information on the man and his work. Admittedly, they are incomplete, but they have served as authentic when much speculation (including my own) needed verification. These papers include business correspondence, press releases, the texts of speeches, drawings, models, contracts, magazine and newspaper articles as well as files on clients other products, or competitors work. Caution is advised. Many contracts were unfulfilled with the designer being paid for his design but with no production resulting. Given the fact that prototypes may have been made as in the Sterling Polynesian line and the Yamato lines, even those empty contracts may be of interest to collectors. With the origins of some of the Syracuse material obscure, it has not been possible to always credit the proper sources. I refer you to these papers emphasizing their importance to any student who would explore Wright's work.

Russel Wright: American Designer is the title of the catalogue written by William J. Hennessey to accompany the New York Gallery Association's Russel Wright exhibit. It is a wonderful overall of all Wright work, beautifully illustrated and quite the most comprehensive work on the subject. It is available from MIT Press. Benjamin Klein published an early writing named *The Collectors Illustrated Price Guide To Russel Wright*. My own *Steubenville Saga*, published before the Syracuse papers became available and my price guide, *Russel Wright and His Dinnerware* were pioneering attempts.

I cannot emphasize enough the importance of my helpful personal conversations with Russel Wright's associates and family. These personal remembrances and recollections have contributed significantly to this work, for only those who knew him best could answer our questions. In many cases, they have been my final authority.

Good News

As I prepare to send this book to the publisher, I've just received wonderful exciting news from Russel's daughter, Annie, and I must include it here.

Annie had been left a life estate in the house Manitoga which we have come to call the familiar name of Dragon Rock. The grounds with nature trails so carefully and delicately scattered were left to the Nature Conservancy. Additionally, a group of friends who understood and shared Wright's love of nature was established as a Board of Trustees with unclear responsibilities, a "just in case" group, one would guess, formed to take responsibility for future possibilities.

Those possibilities have taken on a degree of certainty and the Board, now organized as Manitoga Incorporated, has ownership of both the house and grounds and has developed plans for opening the house, with its furnishings, to the public with the grounds being available for organized nature tours. They are hopeful it will be achieved this year. This project is considered as experimental and if they find it well accepted, intend to build a museum on the grounds which would include a permanent collection of Wright designs.

It is with real pleasure that I have received this news in time to include it here, and my gratitude joins yours, I'm certain, in going out to Annie and Russel's friends who have made this generous gesture. It is fitting and right. Russel would have been pleased that so many of us can now share the interest of his later years.

Two Important Tools For The
Astute Antique Dealer, Collector and Investor

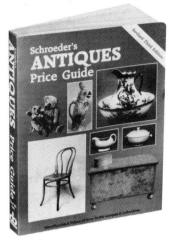

Schroeder's Antiques Price Guide

The very best low cost investment that you can make if you are really serious about antiques and collectibles is a good identification and price guide. We publish and highly recommend **Schroeder's Antiques Price Guide.** Our editors and writers are very careful to seek out and report accurate values each year. We do not simply change the values of the items each year but start anew to bring you an entirely new edition. If there are repeats, they are by chance and not by choice. Each huge edition (it weighs 3 pounds!) has over 56,000 descriptions and current values on 608 - 8½x11 pages. There are hundreds and hundreds of categories and even more illustrations. Each topic is introduced by an interesting discussion that is an education in itself. Again, no dealer, collector or investor can afford not to own this book. It is available from your favorite bookseller or antiques dealer at the low price of $9.95. If you are unable to find this price guide in your area, it's available from Collector Books, P. O. Box 3009, Paducah, KY 42001 at $9.95 plus $1.00 for postage and handling.

Schroeder's INSIDER and Price Update

A monthly newsletter published for the antiques and collectibles marketplace.

The **"INSIDER"**, as our subscribers have fondly dubbed it, is a monthly newsletter published for the antiques and collectibles marketplace. It gives the readers timely information as to trends, price changes, new finds, and market moves both upward and downward. Our writers are made up of a panel of well-known experts in the fields of Glass, Pottery, Dolls, Furniture, Jewelry, Country, Primitives, Oriental and a host of other fields in our huge industry. Our subscribers have that "inside edge" that makes them more profitable. Each month we explore 8-10 subjects that are "in", and close each discussion with a random sampling of current values that are recorded at press

time. Thousands of subscribers eagerly await each monthly issue of this timely 16-page newsletter. A sample copy is available for $3.00 postpaid. Subscriptions are postpaid at $24.00 for 12-months; 24 months for $45.00; 36 months for $65.00. A sturdy 3-ring binder to store your **Insider** is available for $5.00 postpaid. This newsletter contains NO paid advertising and is not available on your newsstand. It may be ordered by sending your check or money order to Collector Books, P. O. Box 3009, Paducah, KY 42001.